TAKEOFF INTO GREATNESS

In the days of early aviation, it was the stunt men and the record setters who seemed to command public attention. Few Americans realized how great an industry was in the making; first by Wright, Curtiss, and Martin, followed by those whose names are recognized today anywhere planes fly—Douglas, Lockheed, Boeing, Cessna, Sikorsky, and many others.

This is the story of the men who built planes for commerce and combat and how they struggled to establish the fact that American-made aircraft were eventually to dominate the skies of the world.

Photo By Harry T. Bishop

Lieutenant Ben H. Wyatt and Grover Loening checking the "1926 Alaska Survey" Loening Amphibian planes before takeoff from San Diego.

Industries of America

TAKEOFF INTO GREATNESS

HOW AMERICAN AVIATION GREW SO BIG SO FAST

By GROVER LOENING

B.Sc., M.A., C.E., Fellow A.I.A.A., R.Ae. Society

G. P. PUTNAM'S SONS

NEW YORK

To my mother
whose early interest in flying
put me on the right beam.

By the Author

Monoplanes and Biplanes—1910 Thesis for degree
Military Aeroplanes—1915 World War I textbook
Our Wings Grow Faster—1935 autobiography

Published simultaneously in the Dominion of
Canada by Longmans Canada Limited, Toronto
Library of Congress Catalog Card Number: 68-15064
PRINTED IN
THE UNITED STATES OF AMERICA
14216

Contents

Smithsonian's National Air and Space Museum

The Wrights' 1904 biplane making the world's first circular flight at Dayton, Ohio, September 1904.

Foreword

In the summer of 1912 a young man recently at the U.S. Naval Academy walked into a small airplane factory on the banks of the Harlem River in New York City. There he met the designer for the Queen Aeroplane Company. The engineer's name was Loening. The former midshipman was this writer.

Now, fifty-six years later, I am privileged to write a Foreword to *Takeoff Into Greatness*. The author, Grover Loening, is now the senior American airplane designer. He is, therefore, well qualified to tell of the unbelievable growth of this fabulous airplane industry.

But more than experience is required to accomplish the magnificent work that Grover has manifested in this book. There must be a human touch, a feel for the many differing personalities in the vast army of able and resolute men who have developed our industry. To write an account, as Loening has, of one of the world's most stupendous technical and business explosions is a privilege that he has merited and that he has won. How fortunate that the writer of this history, at one time Orville Wright's assistant, is here today to tell us what happened, starting almost sixty years ago, and to tell us from personal knowledge, having been involved in this business all that time. He has distinguished himself by his contributions to aviation's inception and to its development by his unremitting toil.

Loening tells in this book about the terrible time the tiny, struggling American aircraft industry had in the First World War. Certain industrial elements in our country, having no knowledge of aircraft, attempted to bypass the few of us who at that time constituted our industry. That they were wrong was attested by their failure and by our later triumphs in an aircraft industry developed by our own bones and sinews—gone on from those pitiful days to days of glory. In response to President Roosevelt's request at the time we entered World War II, we mounted an effort that helped develop the most powerful weapon the world had ever seen—the U.S. Air Force.

After that war our industry turned a large part of its great resources from "swords into plowshares." It has accomplished the greatest transportation breakthrough in history. It has given the world the modern air transport industry and in so doing, we hope, will contribute most importantly to world peace and (as the heir to the Wrights, the Curtisses, the Martins, the Loenings) will forge a dominance in an entirely new worldwide mode of travel. Having been in the forefront of the new and completely different technique of developing space exploration, this same industry will no doubt, in not too many years, be deep in problems of space travel.

Grover Loening's *Takeoff Into Greatness* will, I am sure, be a bridge of understanding for those who will carry on this necessary work, reminding them of the undying debt to distinguished predecessors.

DONALD W. DOUGLAS

Santa Monica, California

Preface

This book is neither a biography nor a recital of historical incidents. It is the story of a great industry by an observer who participated in it. The reader must, therefore, expect to find an understandable amount of personal opinion and appraisement on the part of the author in this story.

The author received much assistance in his project from the personnel of the National Air and Space Museum of the Smithsonian Institution, notably on the part of its head curator, Dr. Paul E. Garber, and its director, S. Paul Johnston—both of whom spent much time in detailed checking of the text. For the photographic material, great assistance was rendered by Ernest W. Robischon and his staff. The Library of Congress, through the courtesy of Dr. Marvin MacFarland, also rendered notable assistance.

Every company in the aircraft industry from whom data or photographs were requested answered promptly.

The text was reviewed and suggestions offered by Dr. Jerome C. Hunsaker, dean emeritus of M.I.T. School of Aeronautics; Admiral Emory S. Land, former president of the Air Transport Association; Dr. Leonard Carmichael, research director of the National Geographic Society; Beckwith Havens, pioneer air pilot; Professor James G. Redfern of Harvard; and Arthur Krock of the *New York Times*—to name only a few of the many friends and associates who materially helped bring reasonable accuracy to the text.

G. L.

Smithsonian's National Air and Space Museum

The *Kitty Hawk*, the first successful flying machine, standing in front of Kill Devil Hill, North Carolina, December 1903.

Smithsonian's National Air and Space Museum

Almost three years after the Wrights' first flight, Santos-Dumont in France managed to get this machine off the ground for a short flight of 82 feet. He was hailed in Europe as the first successful aviator.

1 The Wrights Start It Up

SOME two hundred years ago, poet-philosopher Dr. Samuel Johnson looked into the future with these words: "Instead of the tardy conveyance of ships and chariots, man might use the swifter migration of wings. The fields of air are open to knowledge, and only ignorance and idleness need crawl upon the ground."

The world generally failed to get the message, and for more than seven generations humanity remained patiently tied to the ground, except for balloons. Then the Wrights put their inspired key in the lock and firmly opened the door to the flying era. In the three generations that have since passed, the world has witnessed the breathtaking progress of flying and its growth to maturity. An impressive total of nearly two million factory and airline workers are currently engaged in busily filling the air with thousands of wings that carry the commerce and the wars of nations to the most populous as well as the most remote areas of this little globe. There is more coming. Already we are knocking on the doors of our celestial neighbors . . . confident, daring, unrestrained.

But this has not all been easy. Brief, bitter periods of scorn, ridicule, discouragement and even tragedy had to be surmounted relentlessly before the air industry could achieve its present triumph, accompanied by casual public acceptance and, above all, with a profit to live and grow on.

Here's the story:

The beginning of the air industry's business career may be marked by the occasion in May 1906 when J. P. Morgan and Company in New York paid the Wright brothers 25,000 francs ($5,000). The Wrights had secretly entered into negotiations with a French Government commission for the sale to France of their patents for a total of 1,000,000 francs. They agreed to an option for several months for the sum of 25,000 francs, to be deposited with Morgan and then to be paid to the Wrights if the option were forfeited. It was.

The two brothers had no public relations man giving handouts on their progress in solving the age-old puzzle of flight. But they had a modest, secretive way of their own in letting out just enough information about their activities to whet the appetite of war ministries all over Europe. In the 1903–1907 period, the most singularly apathetic places were Dayton, Ohio, and Washington, D.C.

The French, British and Germans had for several decades been rivaling each other in balloon and gliding aeronautics and in haphazard mechanical flight experimenting and theorizing. Yet all of their attempts at a powered flying machine had failed miserably. Against this background, uncertain rumors had circulated that the Wrights had actually been flying for years. This news was received with ridicule, hostility, disbelief. The majority opinion abroad was that these Dayton "bicycle mechanics" were fakers. Only a few astute experts believed that the 1903–1905 Kitty Hawk, North Carolina, and Dayton, Ohio, flights had really taken place and that the reports were factual and reliable.

The French were the first to give such reports enough credence to send representatives to check up on the stories describing the accomplishment of that impossible feat of rising off the ground and flying on rigid wings. But up to the time of the purchase contract, in early 1906, no Frenchman or representative of the French Government had ever actually seen the Wrights fly.

However, on a visit to Dayton, one of the Frenchmen made inquiries of several witnesses introduced by the Wrights to verify their claims. At the home of one of these witnesses, a small child came into the room and, hearing mention of planes, proceeded to prance around the room and make such noises and graphic gestures imitating flight that the Frenchman was convinced then and there. Why the contract was not completed is a complicated story of intrigue involving French Government officials with ambitions of their own. The Wrights made that $5,000 out of it, anyway; thus paying for many items of wood, wire and fabric needed for further progress.

That same year, 1906, was the one in which the Wright patent, later to be the cause of so much disruptive controversy, was granted, with all its broad claims.

In October 1906, Alberto Santos-Dumont made the first short hop in Europe, a straight jump of 25 meters (82 feet) at Issy Field in Paris. With this he won the first money prize in airplane history—the Archdeacon Prize of the French Aero Club, 4,000 francs. The European world acclaimed this as the real "First Flight of Man." It was witnessed by an enthusiastic crowd, most of whom had not even heard of the Wrights, least of all that the American pioneers had already made scores of flights and had perfected turning maneuvers that had enabled them to end the previous year—1905—with a flight of 24 miles in 38 minutes. The Wrights laughed at this Santos-Dumont jump of 82 feet . . . feeble competition indeed . . . but said nothing.

The French public did not know about the secret dealings of their government with the Wrights earlier in 1906, which had been influenced largely by the pending Moroccan War crisis with Germany.

The very evident difference between the kind of flying that went on in Europe, particularly in France, and the highly successful flying the Wrights had been doing in 1904–1905, was due mainly to one fundamental fact. The pioneers in Europe had not realized the importance (in fact, the absolute necessity) of the third axis control to alter the wing angle to the air laterally at the wing tips, and the effect this would have on turns. Without this lateral control, and with only their rudder for steering and an elevator surface for up-and-down control, the early French planes at first were able to make only hesitant straightaway hops in the calm of a windless dawn.

However, the French made gradual progress, and finally Henri Farman, in a Voisin biplane in January 1907, made the first circular flight in Europe—one kilometer—winning the Deutsch-de-la-Muerthe prize of 10,000 francs. Europe went wild with excitement and France was hailed as the fatherland of flying . . . on a date some two years after the Wrights had been flying such distances as to make all the European flights put together only a fraction of the mileage the Americans had already flown. "These Yankee 'bluffeurs,' they are not to be believed!"

Then came a great change. In August 1908, Wilbur Wright set up his plane on a field at Le Mans, France, near the Léon Bolée automobile factory. As soon as he started to fly, all the world, and the French in particular, knew that the stories and rumors about the Wrights were true and that indeed they had been the first flying men.

The pathetic struggles, short hops, turns of Voisin, Farman, Delagrange, Santos-Dumont, and Ferber were then appraised as childish performances compared to what Wilbur Wright proceeded to show them about flying.

This trip to France involved further development of the first real piece of business the Wrights or anyone else had put on the books. French financiers had reactivated negotiations with

Smithsonian's National Air and Space Museum

Wilbur and Orville Wright in France in January, 1909. Note Orville Wright with cane, still lame from injuries received in the Selfridge accident in Washington, D.C., September 1908.

the Wrights for cash, stock and royalties, for the purpose of forming a French company to take over French rights to those patents that had been adjudicated favorably. Wilbur was there to make on-the-spot demonstrations, which he proceeded to do with a flair, to frenzied public acclaim unrivaled in the past, and not to be equaled until Lindbergh landed in Paris nineteen years later.

All the criticism and disbelief about the American pioneers were forgotten overnight. "Le Grand Wilbur" was the toast . . . the hero . . . the focus of crowds of enthusiasts. Newspapers all over Europe screamed their headlines, waxed lyrical over humanity's winning a battle against gravity. The flying machine, at long last, was a fact, a practical addition to man's conquest of nature!

Wilbur's flights at Le Mans continued for four months through the end of 1908 with no serious accident, even though much of the flying was done in quite windy weather, far different from the early morning calms that the French aviators had been limited to. This impressed observers more than anything else. It demonstrated convincingly the effectiveness of Wilbur's control over his aircraft. French aviator Delagrange admitted, "We are as nothing."

Among the daily visitors and crowds of sightseers that flocked to the Champs d'Auvours (a military field that had been put at the Wrights' disposal) were high public officials, Army officers of many nations, scientists, and numerous aeronautics fans who had been active mainly in ballooning—including Charles Rolls of auto fame, who later flew a Wright.

The hero worship was a nuisance to Wilbur. He was a very taciturn, hermitlike and frugal man. His living arrangements at Le Mans consisted of a small room in the corner of the hangar, where he sought complete privacy while at the same time he could guard his precious plane. To add to the privacy he had the window of this room placed high overhead so no curious visitors could peek in. The annoying intrusiveness of a hero-worshiping public was in vogue even then, decades before motion-picture actors, Lindbergh, or the Beatles.

In his own words Wilbur told the story. "The watchdog that we had obtained was named Flyer and was diligent enough in the daytime, barking at every intruder. We put his doghouse right under the window, so I could hear him at night. Just useless. Peacefully he would sleep on while intruders climbed his doghouse to look in the window. The dog and the doghouse were soon changed."

The American aviator became a legend, much publicized in the French press. As so often happens, the harder it was to interview him, the more extensive the legends became, and the more hundreds of the prying public swarmed around him.

In those months of demonstrations at Le Mans, Wilbur Wright earned an amount of money that was by no means negligible, although he carried no passengers for hire. The Aero Club of the Sarthe offered a prize for flying at an altitude of over 30 meters. Wilbur promptly won it and pocketed 1,000 francs on November 13. Then, five days later, he won another prize offered by the Aero Club de France—2,000 francs more. There were several others, but the climax was his last flight on December 31, 1908 (before moving south to Pau for the winter), when Wilbur Wright won the Prix Michelin, 20,000 francs, by establishing a world's endurance record that was to stand for a long time—flying nonstop for two hours and twenty minutes!

The French contract with the Wrights required the training of three pupils. The first of these was the Count de Lambert, who had his first lesson in October 1908. He became a proficient pilot, electrifying the Parisian public a few months later by flying his Wright plane over Paris and circling the Eiffel Tower for the first time in a heavier-than-air machine.

The pioneering of the Wrights in the invention of a practical flying machine was only one of their telling contributions to the start of the airplane industry. The 1908 demonstrations at Le Mans had awakened the world to the realization that aviation was here to stay, and had a tremendous future.

Whenever anyone would question the practical use of flying machines, Wilbur would recall Benjamin Franklin's famous

Smithsonian's National Air and Space Museum

King Alfonso of Spain inspecting the plane with Wilbur Wright at Pau, France, February 1909.

comment when witnessing Montgolfier's first balloon ascent. To the question "What good are these balloons?" Franklin, first U.S. minister to France, said, "My friend, I answer your question with another. What good is a newborn child?"

The brothers from Dayton thought the use of planes in war would be largely for observation. Even at a later date, when the destructiveness of air power became so devastating, Orville Wright often expressed horror and regret that their creation had also found its way into such terrible activities.

In 1909, the flights in Europe were moved to Pau, in the south of France, where the acclaim of the Wrights continued. The heads of most governments visited there to see for themselves this "miracle," as Lord Northcliffe called it. King Edward VII of England, King Alfonso of Spain, lesser royalty, prime ministers, all found their way to Pau. There they learned that these modest American geniuses were not uncouth "mechanics," as they had at first been pictured, but socially delightful and refined gentlemen. Orville and his sister Katherine, who was called "Schwesterchen" by her brothers, joined Wilbur at Pau in a very worldly atmosphere dominated by the American railroad tycoon Frederick Prince (whose son Norman would in a few years become a hero and war casualty of the Lafayette Escadrille).

Everyone learned how upstanding this Dayton family was. Father Wright was a bishop and the mother was of aristocratic German extraction. This gave tone to the business developments then starting in aviation—the highest kind of ethics—and explains why the Wrights were so successful in attracting the finest names in American banking and industry. It also explains why they were so agonizingly upset by sharp practices in the later exhibition phase of promotion, and by the stealing of their inventive labors by patent infringers. Explained too is why the Wrights would not allow any flying on Sunday, even in later years, when they lost much exhibition money to others less strict.

The prestige of American aviation got a tremendous boost by the visit of the Wrights to Europe. American public ignorance of their work changed to mild interest.

While Wilbur was in Europe, Orville stayed in the United States to fly the *Model A* which, after many disappointing delays, had been ordered by the U.S. Army in February 1908. Along with rapid technical progress came an increasing number of accidents to other fliers, some serious, a few fatal. Yet the glamor of the Wrights was not tarnished significantly by these misfortunes.

Their European activities continued into Italy, where they sold a plane to the Italian Government. They progressed into Germany, also with outstanding success. For these visits the biplane was folded easily, then mounted on a wheeled dolly and rolled into a freight car for shipping over distances too long for towing by road.

Meanwhile, the other part of the Wrights' 1908 two-ring circus, which was so entrancing to the world, was underway at Fort Myer, Virginia, near Washington, D.C. This was the demonstration and official testing of the U.S. Army's first airplane order. The story of how the Army finally procured the plane after many years of stalling is appallingly similar to the bureaucratic red tape that hampers new proposals to this very day. A shocking series of apathetic turndowns, with no intelligent appraisals and a stubborn disbelief that the early flights had even taken place, came after the Wrights had written to their Congressman on January 18, 1905. The letter read in part:

> The series of aeronautical experiments upon which we have been engaged for the past five years has ended in the production of a flying-machine of a type fitted for practical use . . . and suitable for scouting. [The one hundred and five flights made in Dayton in 1904 were then described, including two five-minute flights complete with controlled turns and landings with no difficulty; air speed about 35 miles an hour and flights made in calm or in winds. . . .] If you can find . . . whether this is . . . of interest to our own government, it would oblige us greatly . . . and aid us in making our plans for the future.

This letter was forwarded to the Secretary of War and then to the Ordnance Department, which answered a few weeks later, ". . . so many requests have been made for financial assistance in the development of flying machines, the Board has found it necessary to decline to make allotments for the experimental development of devices for mechanical flight . . ." and more to the same effect. Just a crude brushoff. The Wrights were understandably upset, as they had not asked for a cent and had already perfected the "devices."

It is incredible, viewed from this distance, that the Government dismissed this offer of a possibly deadly war innovation without even sending a young lieutenant to investigate this

Signal Corps, United States Army.

These Articles of Agreement entered into this --------tenth---------- day of February---, nineteen hundred and-eight--, between ----Chas. S. Wallace----, Captain------------------, Signal Corps, United States Army, of the first part, and

Wilbur and Orville Wright, trading as Wright Brothers, of 1127 West Third Street, Dayton,

in the county of--------Montgomery-----------, State of ------Ohio-----------, of the second part, WITNESSETH, that in conformity with copy of the advertisement, specifications, and proposal hereunto attached, and which, in so far as they relate to this contract, form a part of it, the said --------------------Chas. S. Wallace, Captain,----------------- Signal Corps, United States Army, for and in behalf of the United States of America, and the said ---------------------------Wright Brothers-------------------------- (hereinafter designated as the contractor) do covenant and agree, to and with each other, as follows, viz:

ARTICLE I. That the said contractor shall manufacture for and deliver to the United States of America,

One (1) heavier-than-air flying machine, in accordance with Signal Corps Specification No. 486, dated December 23, 1907.

ART. II. That the deliveries of the supplies and materials herein contracted for shall be made in the manner, numbers, or quantities, and for each number or quantity, on or before the date specified therefor, as follows, viz:

That complete delivery shall be made on or before August 28, 1908.

IN WITNESS WHEREOF the parties aforesaid have hereunto placed their hands the date first hereinbefore written.

WITNESSES:

John J. Mullaney as to Chas. S. Wallace, Captain Signal Corps, U. S. Army.

Albert Lariviere as to

C. E. Taylor as to Wright Brothers by Orville Wright

H. G. Hoffman as to

APPROVED: FEB 28 1908, 190

James Allen
Brigadier General,
Chief Signal Officer of the Army.

U.S. War Department

The original Wright contract of 1908 with the U.S. Army—first of its kind.

pioneering. Meanwhile, as occasional publicity items filtered through the quasi-secret status that the Wrights maintained about the many flights made at Dayton in 1904 and continuing in 1905, the British took a sudden interest in negotiating for the Wright *Flyer*. On February 11, 1905, a letter from the British War Office asked for terms. Discussions went on for several months. The Wrights finally realized that the British were just prolonging the dickering to learn more about their progress while paying nothing.

A second approach to Washington was made October 19, 1905. Again the same negative answer was received from the Ordnance Board. This time, however, the questionable word "requirements," that absurd, often-hated word (that later Air Force personnel were to use so frequently as a lame excuse) entered the aircraft vocabulary for the first time. Ordnance answered that there were "no requirements" and that "'the Board does not care to formulate any requirements for the performance of a flying-machine until a machine is produced for horizontal flight . . . to carry an operator . . . and drawings furnished, to show the construction."

In other words, they were requesting plans of an already proven machine in order to determine whether or not it could possibly fly. Wilbur decided to direct his efforts at those willing to buy. At the same time, he was determined to keep knocking persistently at the War Department's door.

This is exactly what they did in due course, but in a different way. Godfrey Cabot, a leading Boston capitalist, and later one of the most ardent supporters and benefactors of aeronautics, had heard at that early date (March 1906) from the Wrights about their treatment by the Army. He was so outraged that he took it up with his relative, Senator Henry Cabot Lodge of Massachusetts. Here we encounter at the start the familiar Washington system for getting contracts. Senator Lodge put pressure on the War Department, but not until several other persons had also nudged the Army to take some action. For many months nothing more happened. Meanwhile, the

Wrights were improving their engine and getting ready to assemble some new planes for 1907, sensing correctly that a busy time was ahead.

Obviously the Ordnance Board had finally heard from "higher up," and on May 11, 1907, came the first real break in the U.S. aviation stalemate. A letter came from Washington saying that the board would be glad to receive a proposal from the Wright Cycle Company. The Wrights answered with a bid of $100,000 for the first machine. They were told the price was too high and the Army would have to get a special appropriation from the Congress at its next session. More months of delay. By November 1907, Wilbur had come back from a trip to Europe that had to do with more patent negotiations. At once he held conferences in Washington with the Army for the first time. He reduced his price to $25,000 for one machine that was to fly at 40 miles per hour, carry a passenger, have fuel for 125 miles (requirements well within what the Wrights had already done in their secret tests). No patent rights were included in this bid.

The story of America's first aircraft procurement sounds exactly like the system in vogue thirty or forty years later. The same angles, delays, excuses, both by the Government and the eager contractors. Instead of ordering at once from the Wrights, the Army advertised for bids, using the Wrights' promised performances as their requirement.

To the astonishment of everyone, two proper, paid-up bids besides the one from Dayton were received. There was quite a hassle as a result. The other bidders, lower than the Wrights, were A. M. Herring of New York and J. F. Scott of Chicago, both with theoretical flying experience only, though Herring had some gliding experience. He was later to join Glenn Curtiss in the Herring-Curtiss Company. The Aerial Experiment Association, of which much will be heard, did not put in a bid, but about forty cranks did. These were thrown out because they did not have the required 10 percent deposit. How to get around the Scott and Herring bids? A trick solution to this impasse was approved by President Theodore Roosevelt. His emergency fund was made available to buy the two other planes in addition to the Wright *Flyer* if they met the performance required. In short order, the others dropped out for various reasons, and on February 8, 1908, the Wright bid was legally accepted and signed, the first competitive aircraft contract in the history of U. S. aviation.

Though the Wrights themselves had done no flying since 1905, they had made many improvements in their aircraft, not only in developing a four-cylinder upright motor with fuel injection, but also in building the pilot's seat and controls so that he could sit vertically instead of lying prone on the wings, as he had in the original *Kitty Hawk* of 1903 and the later version of 1904. There were other changes to the rudders and fins.

The Army contract stipulated that the acceptance tests were to be made at the Army post at Fort Myer, Virginia, just across the river from Washington, delivery to be made in late August 1908.

In characteristically thorough manner, the Wrights returned in May to Kitty Hawk to test and practice with their latest plane, which they called the *Model A*. They fully tested their new engine with its upright cylinders, the one later to become so familiar to the aviation world. They were bedeviled by newspapermen who had awakened at last to the fact that vital history was being made on the Carolina sands. Headlines and excitement abounded, but the sensational press had its first disappointment . . . there were no fatal accidents. On this occasion the first flights with two men were made, and under perfect control in increasingly strong winds.

The plane destined for the Army arrived at Fort Myer, and by September 3, 1908, the plane was set up and Orville was ready for his first public demonstration flight. It had been decided that Wilbur was to sail for France for their show there. He had already been there a week or so and the two widely separated exhibits became headline rivals for whatever news attention the inventors of the airplane were at last com-

U.S. Army
The folded Wright plane arriving at Fort Myer on an Army wagon.

manding. The future held acclaim for Wilbur, but only stark tragedy for Orville.

There was less newspaper excitement about the Fort Myer flights than there had been about the flights at Kitty Hawk a few months before. But, of course, all the important people in the Capitol were visiting the field, thrilled to see this controversial and heretofore secret machine doing its stuff before their eyes. Among the visitors was the great scientist and inventor Alexander Graham Bell, and with him a young Army lieutenant, Thomas A. Selfridge. Dr. Bell had experimented successfully with flying, man-carrying kites, and then had joined with Glenn Curtiss, of motorcycle fame, and others in forming the Aerial Experiment Association. As already noted, this group was to become significantly active in the year ahead. Selfridge, too, was a member. As they had represented to Orville that they were only researching, with no thought of profit, they were cordially greeted by him at the Wright hangar.

His demonstrations proceeded from one flight to another,

U.S. War Department

Orville Wright and Lt. Selfridge, ready for takeoff. The plane is mounted on the wooden catapult rail.

The Army's first plane wreck at Fort Myer, September 17, 1908. The man with the straw hat is Lorin Wright.

Associated Press

each higher and longer, Orville circling the field with such grace and ease that the crowd gasped in ever-increasing astonishment. Finally, on September 12, the Chief Signal Officer of the Army, Maj. George O. Squier, flew with Orville for over nine minutes, establishing a new world's record for passenger carrying. Following this, Orville circled the field faultlessly 71 consecutive times at a height of about 300 feet, setting a new endurance record of 1 hour and 15 minutes nonstop. Doubts in America about the Wrights' flying vanished that day.

The final flight of this series was made a few days later, on September 17. Lt. Frank Lahm, a great and helpful friend of the Wrights, had made an earlier flight with Orville on a previous day, and so it became the turn of Lt. Selfridge to be the Army observer on the next flight. This was just what the young lieutenant had hoped for, because of his current interest and activity with Curtiss, Dr. Bell and others of the Aerial Experiment Association.

The Wright catapult weight was hoisted to the top of the starting tower, and the plane was set on its dolly on the 100-foot track. The aviators took their seats, Orville released the holding catch, and the falling weight pulled the craft rapidly along the rail; in seconds they were off in free flight with smooth acceleration. After about three turns of the field, the spectators saw the plane lurch, heard the engine shut off, watched the plane head for a bush-filled gully. A sharp twisting of the wings caused the plane to turn toward the field and it looked as if a safe landing could be made, but the machine suddenly went into a dive. Orville reported later that he lost control, and just before hitting the ground it seemed for a few seconds that it would be righted. But it hit too soon, demolishing the plane and throwing both occupants out to pile up with the wreckage in a cloud of dust. Groans came from the horrified witnesses. The photo newsmen jumped fast on this occasion and even got some action pictures. Had there been television at that date, what a special showing this would have made! When the wreckage was examined and the accident studied, it was determined that a propeller had sheared off a wire bracing the tail boom. Orville Wright was severly injured with a fractured leg, broken ribs, and a back injury that bothered him for the rest of his life. As for Selfridge, his skull was fractured and he suffered other internal injuries from which he died a few hours later, the first American Army air casualty in a long and honored list that was to stretch through the years—martyrs to the advancing cause of conquering the air.

When Wilbur heard of this fatal break in their progress, he stopped flying for a day or two, and his French associates sensed his profound grief. They all knew, however, that he and Orville would both feel that "the show must go on," as indeed it did, with Wilbur continuing alone until Orville was sufficiently recovered by January 1909 to join him in France. There was little discouragement or fear as a result of this sad occurrence, just a firm determination to fly ever better and more safely. That same spirit has pervaded aviation ever since. The gallant behavior of these early pioneers served as a guiding light.

Many other steps in aviation's growth were now being taken. Only incidentally does history record that on June 28, 1909, Orville Wright was back in Washington, again performing his acceptance trials in compliance with the Army contract on a new and improved machine. A month later the tests were concluded with a notable cross-country flight, the first in America. Orville Wright and Lt. Benjamin Foulois (the famous and beloved "Benny," who later became Chief of the Air Corps) flew from Fort Myer to a hill near Alexandria, Virginia, and returned at a speed of over 42 miles an hour in a strong, gusty wind. This speed, which exceeded the requirement, earned them a bonus of $5,000.

The Army promptly paid the Wrights the $30,000 due them and the first Government contract was a successfully closed piece of business. Over the next half-century this tiny beginning was to grow to procurement by the U. S. Government of many billions of dollars' worth of aircraft a year!

2 Curtiss Next in Line

THE INVENTOR of the telephone, great scientist that he was, went far afield and off the beam when he branched out into flying efforts. Surprisingly, Alexander Graham Bell overlooked or perhaps had no conception of certain aerodynamic fundamentals that the Wrights had secretly developed, such as knowing where the center of the air force pressure would be on a plane surface presented at an angle to the wind in order to get a lift out of it. Nor did he know apparently about interference and streamlining—how airflow was so tenuous a medium that it cohered and flowed together like water up to sonic speed.

Dr. Bell independently, somewhat secretly, conducted experiments at Baddeck, Nova Scotia, actually aimed at constructing a real flying machine. What a hopeless concept it was has never been adequately examined. His "Tetrahedral" construction was a mass of triangular cells, strong to be sure, but with a built-in drag and head resistance that would kill any prospects for efficient lift. No thought at all had been given to the control of sideways tilting, for lateral balance in turns.

This strange "research" effort of Bell's in man-carrying kites

A. M. Benwer Collection

Bell *Cygnet* No. 2 built at Baddeck, Nova Scotia in February 1909. J. A. D. McCurdy made a short hop with this plane. There was no lateral control.

could be dismissed as of no consequence in aviation development, were it not for the group of dedicated young men that he gathered about him. First there was Lt. Thomas Selfridge, already mentioned, the young friend of Mr. and Mrs. Bell's; and J. A. D. McCurdy and F. W. (Casey) Baldwin, two young Canadian sportsmen, adventurous skiers and engineers in their early twenties. These two hardly were types who would be likely to find in flying only a dull field for "pure research."

Assisted financially by Mrs. Bell, this group in October 1907 organized the Aerial Experiment Association, with Selfridge as secretary. Like many others all over the world, they too had heard the rumors about the Wrights.

Bell's man-carrying kite-flying efforts included towing the kite on the water or on ice to get airborne. Soon the group needed a light motor for flight trials. But motors were scarce. In Hammondsport, New York, was Glenn Curtiss, who had become a well-known motorcycle racer using his own machines with a light 8-cylinder, 40 horsepower motor built by himself. He also had built engines light enough for Captain Tom Baldwin's dirigible balloons. It was quite natural that the Baddeck group should make contact with Curtiss to procure a motor. They went much further. Curtiss was made a member of their association with the title of Director of Experiments, and their activities were moved to Hammondsport, New York, on the shores of Lake Keuka. Hydroairplane development there was a natural step, as the future was soon to disclose.

Perhaps the fact that Curtiss had visited the Wrights the year before to discuss motors, and had been cordially received as well as shown many pictures of their flights, may have influenced Bell in making Curtiss so important a part of his efforts. As already indicated, Bell and his group at the outset repeatedly represented that they were only doing research experiments, with no thought of business or profit. The Wrights believed this, with a naïveté conspicuously absent in later years. No doubt developing circumstances justifiably changed the point of view of Bell, Curtiss and their associates as the year progressed.

The Wrights had discovered several "secrets" about flying, in addition to the necessity of the third control for lateral tilting. Proper balance of a plane required knowing where the center of the air force was located so that weights could be placed in balance. Instead of flat surfaces for the wings, curved sections were used, since these arched surfaces had more lift—all very evident when the curved cross section of a bird's wing is examined. Up to the time of the Wrights it had been assumed that the center of air pressure on such curved sections moved as in flat planes from the midpoint forward to the front edge, as the angle to the wind decreased. But the Wrights made no such assumption, and in careful testing they discovered that this center of the air forces actually moved backward in the important flying angle region as the angle decreased. The center of lift which this air force generated was therefore disastrously different in its location, and had to be allowed for.

This almost certainly had been the reason for the crash of the Langley *Aerodrome* in 1903. The wings had not been braced for lifting forces so much farther back than Langley and others at the time supposed. A study of the photos and the wing structure indicates that when the catapult acceleration forced the airflow onto the wings, they folded up. This was surely a contributing reason for the repeated dumping of the Langley *Aerodrome* into the Potomac River.

How else can we appraise what then happened, except to note that the Wrights were imposed upon indeed when Selfridge wrote to them on January 15, 1908:

> I am taking the liberty of writing you and asking your advice on certain points connected with gliding experiments . . .
>
> Will you kindly tell me what results you obtained on the travel of the center of pressure both on aerocurves and aeroplanes?
>
> I hope I am not asking too much by asking you these questions.

To this Orville answered obligingly by giving him the pertinent data and other references. In later years the Wrights were very adamant in claiming that they gave Curtiss the key to success with this priceless information. That they helped by being so affable is quite certain.

Things moved quickly at Hammondsport after this. The first airplane of the Aerial Experiment Association, called the *Red Wing*, with "Casey" Baldwin as pilot, on March 18, 1908, flew a short 319 feet over the ice, crashing on landing. It had no lateral control, but it was balanced. The next plane, the *White Wing*, designed by Baldwin, did have movable sections on the wing ends for lateral control. Curtiss flew this over 1,000 feet straightaway on May 22. Then Selfridge flew it, becoming the first military officer in the world to fly a plane. The third plane of this group, designed by Curtiss, was called the *June Bug*. It was a success.

The first officially witnessed flight in the United States was made with the *June Bug* by Glenn Curtiss on July 4, 1908. On this flight he won the Scientific American Trophy for the first-prize flight of over one kilometer. He actually flew 4,000 feet at 34 miles per hour. The Wrights had flown this far four years

Smithsonian's National Air and Space Museum

The *June Bug* in flight. Note ailerons at the wing tips for lateral control; not very effective.

The *June Bug* on a flight for the Scientific American Trophy, July 4, 1908. Standing left to right: A. M. Herring, "Casey" Baldwin, Glenn Curtiss, Dr. C. M. Manly, Stanley Beach, J. A. D. McCurdy.

Smithsonian's National Air and Space Museum

earlier. Twenty months previously they had flown more than sixty times farther!

The *June Bug* flights by Curtiss started off with a lot of publicity. However, no reference was made to any kind of assistance from the Wright brothers. Naturally, the Wrights resented it, and at this point the hostility and bitterness that were to characterize the next few years probably started.

Orville Wright had written Curtiss in July, 1908:

> I learn from the *Scientific American* that your *June Bug* has movable surfaces at the tips of the wings, adjustable to different angles for maintaining lateral balance. In our letter to Lieutenant Selfridge of January 18th replying to his of the 15th, in which he asked for information on the construction of 'flyers' . . . we did not intend to give permission to use patented features of our machine for exhibitions or in a commercial way . . .
>
> If it is your desire to enter the exhibition business, we would be glad to take up the matter of a license to operate under our patents for that purpose.

Curtiss replied, a few days later:

> Contrary to newspaper reports we do not expect to do anything in the way of exhibitions; these flights have been in connection with the work of the Aerial Experiment Association.

Early in the year 1909, and after Bell had witnessed the Wright flights at Fort Myer, the Aerial Experiment Association was disbanded. Early the next year, Curtiss began forming a new company. Lieutenant Selfridge was destined not to be a part of it. The reward for his pioneering had been death at Fort Myer, where he flew as a passenger with Orville in the very machine he and his associates had been trying to emulate.

Despite earlier denials, aeronautics had so changed that Curtiss proceeded to embark on a brilliant career of commercial and exhibition flying development, with a flair for publicity that far outdid the Wrights' and a courage to face unknown flying dangers at least the equal of theirs. His flying ability, however, never equaled Orville's.

The Wrights' great haul of prizes, publicity and acclaim in Europe and finally in the United States in 1908 and early 1909 were soon rivaled by Glenn Hammond Curtiss. By June 1909 he had organized a new company with A. M. Herring, a glider experimenter with Octave Chanute in Chicago and an engineer (bidder for an Army contract in 1908), and with Courtlandt F. Bishop, a capitalist. It was called the Herring-Curtiss Company; it had $360,000 in capital stock and some cash. They started seriously in business, despite Curtiss' early protestations . . . Wright patent notwithstanding.

On June 26, 1909, the first commercial sale of a plane in America was effected, when Curtiss delivered the airplane ordered by the Aeronautic Society of New York. This society had a group of rich "air enthusiasts," no doubt publicity seekers in part, but quite helpful in this practical instance. Among the leaders of this group were Stanley Beach of the *Scientific American*; Peter Cooper Hewitt, a scientist; William Hammer, a noted engineer; and Lee Burroughs, a banker. Together they had raised the needed $7,500 to buy this Curtiss airplane—a direct development of the 1908 *June Bug*. With a difference . . . this one had Herring's type of separately mounted interplane ailerons for lateral control, presumed by Curtiss to avoid the Wright patent. It was this sale that triggered the violent and determined patent suit by the Wrights to prevent Curtiss from doing business without a license.

The occasion of the setting up and first flight of the Curtiss biplane at Morris Park Racetrack, near New York, was exciting and memorable to many people soon to be prominently identified with flying developments. These included Augustus Post and Capt. Tom Baldwin, balloonists, and Charles F. Willard, the first civilian to be a Curtiss pupil, and myself. Willard later became a noted exhibition flyer, then one of America's leading designers, a builder of planes, and a test pilot.

There were many other airplane contraptions at Morris Park that day, including a weird multi-propeller design built by Dr. Wilbur R. Kimball. This one was christened, champagne and all, by the then famous musical comedy star Anna Held . . . none of which helped it fly. It didn't. When it finally got started it slewed around into a fence. The publicity featured Anna Held's fantastic dress and huge picture hat, but no mention of the fence.

When the wind and the excitement had died down, Curtiss flew a resolute circle over the track at a height of about 30 feet, landing in good order amid the genuine enthusiasm of the awed onlookers. In succeeding days many more flights were made and trophies won. All this was suitably recorded by a willing and eager press, who were closely following this occasion. The day of the exhibition meet had dawned, and in populous New York to boot.

In the story of how rapidly the aviation business was to grow, the years 1909–1911 assumed a very great importance. During this period the surge of activity reached a crest of immense affluence for many of the early pioneers. This was due chiefly to the rivalry among the great newspaper organizations in featuring front page exclusives in the interest of circulation and back page advertising. Many papers offered huge prizes for feats of flying.

The public had become frantic about air-stunt sensations. The disbelief and scorn that had prevailed for a decade gave way to demands for more and more demonstrations that flying had really arrived. Public appetite was whetted, to be sure, by an occasional fatal accident, headlined on the front page. The detractors of flying had many fine chances for an "I told you so," and the press had a field day, keeping the readers on edge in morbid anticipation.

On July 25, 1909, the world was electrified by the news that Louis Bleriot had flown the English Channel, a feat not to be surpassed in import until Lindbergh's transatlantic flight eighteen years later. The big air meets, growing constantly in num-

Brown Brothers

Louis Bleriot lands on a hillside near Dover, England.

ber, were crowded with eager customers, both in the United States and abroad, who paid for admission by the tens of thousands.

Glenn Curtiss led the parade by showing up at the last minute at the first International Air Meet at Rheims, France, to fly for the Gordon Bennett Speed Trophy. With it went $10,000 in cash, donated by the *Paris Herald*. On August 29, to the great surprise of the French entries and the public (and to the dismay of the Wrights, who also had an entry), Curtiss led the field around a 20-kilometer course at a speed of 47.4 miles an hour. This would have been some eight or ten miles an hour faster than the Wright machine could have done. That excellent little 8-cylinder engine, the ancestor of the famous OX-5, delivered its 50 horsepower without a miss—almost twice as much power as competing engines, foreign or domestic, could produce.

From then on, in all aviation activities, the race was to the swiftest. It was Louis Bleriot himself who stated in an interview: "The only *raison d'être* of flying is speed. Slow aircraft will never amount to much." The future, that so soon was to be commanded by the sleekest planes with the biggest engines, showed how true were his prescient words.

On Curtiss' return from this epic victory, he and Wilbur

Wright tangled at the same time on the occasion of the flying exhibitions for the Hudson-Fulton Celebration in New York at the end of September 1909. They had separate hangars on the large parade ground of the Army post at Governor's Island. Early on the morning of September 29, having obtained a pass from the banker August Belmont (then close to the Wrights), I went there, cutting college to do so. It was a very foggy dawn with no wind. Wilbur, waiting for the thick blanket to lift, was sitting in his plane practicing controls with imaginary displacements. (Flying training on the ground years later in the Link trainer often reminded one of Wright's version of it.) After a while we could hear Curtiss across the field warming up his engine. He did more than this; he could be heard taxiing up and down the field, sometimes quite close to our side. Wilbur agreed that there was no indication he had taken off, merely shrugged, mumbling, "No wind to help take off." But Curtiss had a busy, ingenious, and one might say imaginative "publicity" man (P.R. was not yet in the language). For what should appear in the early editions of the papers but the featured story that Curtiss had made an "Early Morning Flight Around the Statue of Liberty." When he read it later, Wilbur Wright was more than slightly infuriated. After the fog had lifted, Wright took to the air with ease into a helping wind, headed out over the bay, and proceeded to circle the Statue of Liberty, watched by thousands from the Battery and the skyscraper windows of lower New York.

A few days later, on October 4, Wilbur Wright made his epic flight up the Hudson River to Grant's Tomb, circled it, and returned. The millions of New York City watched breathlessly, many fearing a falter or crash. But, no . . . the heavier-than-air machine went serenely on its way, sure and steady, inspiring unexpected confidence. Most of the next day's papers never even mentioned Curtiss' attempts, so this round went to the Wrights.

Whether because of New York's location or its function as the business hub of America, the focus of aviation's advance

Franklin Institute

Wilbur Wright's Hudson River flight. The canoe is for safety over water.

Associated Press

Curtiss plane at Governor's Island, New York.

and its accompanying business activities from 1909 to 1914 seemed to center predominantly around that city. If the great metropolitan newspapers had not indulged in their prize-offering fever, we can readily imagine what we would have missed in terms of epoch-making feats of the flying men of that day, and the profound influence their activities had on aeronautical design, on public acceptance, and on the raising of financial backing.

What these newspaper-prize incentives meant to the earnings and yearnings of the aviation business of that day was formidable, indeed. The prizes reached a total of over $200,000 for the years 1909–1911.

Gordon-Bennett Race (*N.Y. Paris Herald*) at Rheims Air Meet, won by Glenn Curtiss, August 29, 1909 .... $10,000

The *New York World* prize—for flight from Albany to New York, won by Glenn Curtiss, May 29, 1910 10,000

Philadelphia Ledger-New York Times prize—New York to Philadelphia, won by C. K. Hamilton (Curtiss), June 13, 1910 10,000

So far, Curtiss was running away with the honors and the money, to the consternation of the Wright aviators. But they caught up.

Atlantic City newspapers prize for altitude reached, won by Walter Brookins, 6,700 feet (Wright), July 9, 1910 .... $ 5,000

St. Louis Post Dispatch-N.Y. World prize for New York to St. Louis flight, offered at this time and, months later, won by Harry Atwood (Wright) ... 30,000

Boston Globe prize for flight around Boston Light, won by Grahame-White (Bleriot), September 15,

1910, at the stimulating Harvard Flying Meet at Squantum Meadows 10,000

Baltimore Sun prize for first flight over Baltimore, won by Hubert Latham in French *Antoinette,* November 7, 1910 5,000

New York Journal-William Randolph Hearst prize for first flight across the United States from east to west or west to east, which Cal Rodgers (Wright) did, but lost the money by exceeding 30 days, September 17 to December 10, 1911 50,000

New York Times prize for flight from New York to Chicago—in keen competition for over a year, finally made by Harry Atwood in 1912, in his Wright *Model B* 25,000

All over the country, many smaller prizes were offered by papers in local communities, vying for the kudos of being flight patrons. Often these prizes were won, sometimes not—as in the cross-country Hearst prize. A tantalizing incentive, anyhow. Added to all this was the biggest source of income of all—the great air meets and the innumerable smaller exhibition flying dates for cash contracts and prizes.

The January 1910 Los Angeles Air Meet started with a total prize offering of $50,000. This was followed by a similar purse for the Chicago Meet in August. A month later the Boston Air Meet raised its prize offering to $92,000. With this much inducement, many foreign flyers began to take part, encouraged by the arrangement the managers of this meet had made with the Wrights to protect the contestants from patent harassment by paying the Wrights a flat fee of $30,000. Early in October, 1910, the St. Louis Air Meet took place, followed by the greatest meet of all, starting October 22, the International Meet at Belmont Park, New York. This meet also paid a royalty to the Wrights. Here was staged the second speed competition for the Gordon-Bennett Speed Trophy Race, won by Claude Grahame-

Paul Batt Aeronautical Collection

Glenn L. Martin in his very strongly constructed pusher type of exhibition machine, built by himself. Powered by a Curtiss engine, it was at the time considered the best constructed aircraft in use.

White at 61 miles per hour. The year previously it had been won by Curtiss, at 47.4 miles per hour. The total money won on this historic occasion was over $100,000.

Many successful aviators, such as Grahame-White, Sopwith, the French teams, and the Wright and Curtiss teams, participated in one big or little meet after another. They more than made expenses by earning real money with which to order better and faster planes. By then planes were costing $5,000 to $7,000 each. Thus did the meets give a vital stimulus to the airplane manufacturing industry that was stumblingly emerging into reality. In 1911 this hectic activity continued, the high point being marked by the Chicago International Air Meet. Again over $100,000 was available for the contestants to vie for. Europe had much the same story to tell and with the same accent on newspaper sponsorship. Notable was the London to

Paul Batt
Aeronautical Collection
Lincoln Beachey, star of the exhibition era and the first in America to loop the loop.

Manchester Race in 1910, won by Louis Paulhan, French aviator, with a $50,000 *London Daily Mail* prize. Various "circuits" and record prizes were fathered by press associations and aero clubs. In France in particular, some of the huge prizes were established by the Government obviously for military advancement.

By the end of 1911, the Wrights and Curtiss were meeting important rivals. Glenn Martin from Los Angeles, California, Starling Burgess from Marblehead, Massachusetts, and several others were building good airplanes that could in many instances outdo the earlier pioneers. The speed record had been raised to over 83 miles per hour by Nieuport, in France. The altitude record of 11,642 feet was established by Beachey at Chicago on August 20, 1911. The endurance record was increased to over four hours nonstop by Howard Gill, in a Wright *B*.

From the half-dozen flying men of 1909 the flying fraternity grew rapidly. By the end of 1911 there were 82 American pilots licensed by the then-established Aero Club in New York to take part in air meets. At least 50 more Americans were unlicensed but had flown solo. The flying fatalities were shocking. Almost a fifth of this number had been killed or severely injured. It is to the everlasting credit of the aviation people of that era that, chagrined as they were by these tragedies, they kept on with their developments. The vision was not to be dimmed by discouraging setbacks; by the loss of such outstanding flying virtuosos as Ralph Johnstone, Arch Hoxsey, and John Moisant of monoplane fame. Eugene Ely, before his untimely death at an exhibition, had made the first real Naval advance by landing on and flying from an improvised wooden deck of the battleship *Pennsylvania*. Harriet Quimby, leading aviatrix, was also an accident victim. The Army and Navy added their quota to this sad account. First killed, after Selfridge, was Lt. G. E. Kelly. Then came in too rapid succession, Love, Post, Ellington, Rich, Rockwell of the Army; Murray, Billingsley from the Navy. Many of our permanent airfields are named after these pioneer heroes. It was Ralph Johnstone, who, when asked about the danger of flying, remarked two months before his death, "It's going to get us all. The non-man-killing airplane of the future will be created from our crushed bones."

Nevertheless, business interests all over the country, particularly in New York, now began to get excited about the profit possibilities of aviation. A tremendous amount of money flowed in from the astonishing growth of the exhibition business. The Wright Company in the year 1911–12 earned over $1,000,000 in exhibition fees, in air-meet participation, and in the few sales made to private individuals. Curtiss did almost as well. At many of the meets all the aviators were paid two dollars a minute for their flight time—a sure way to provide a lot of flying for the spectators. The usual fee for a small county fair ranged from $2,000 to $5,000 for a day or two. And so

Lawrence Gichener

Glenn Martin and Mary Pickford in his tractor type of biplane.

many of them demanded appearances that both Wright and Curtiss had to build a large organization for business management and for overseeing the pilots. Nor was it long before many of the professional flyers branched out on their own.

Glenn L. Martin, the most serious and ambitious rival of Wright and Curtiss, was branching out rapidly in Los Angeles. This twenty-one-year-old auto salesman and manager of a garage saw the light of aviation's future as early as 1909. He set about building a monoplane type with a modified Ford motor. This cracked up on its first try. By August 1909 he had built a Curtiss-type biplane, succeeded in making short hops, and finally flew across the fence of the field he was using and landed in another field. Then with a new three-cylinder Elbridge engine in his biplane, he began making longer and longer flights with well-executed turns. Martin taught himself to fly. He had no teacher and was further handicapped by bad eyesight. Californians knew of his flying attempts and he suffered much ridicule, but he kept on under strained financial circumstances. On December 20, 1909, he entered his biplane in the First International Air Meet at Dominguez Field near Los Angeles. After some balky motor difficulties, he ended the meet by circling in the air for twelve and a half minutes, winning a prize for his feat. Then he started building a new pusher biplane with a Curtiss engine, having decided deliberately to win enough money in exhibitions to set himself up in a factory where he could enter the business of manufacturing planes. Starting in an old church at Santa Ana, Martin soon moved into a loft factory in Los Angeles. By 1913 he had added two exceptionally able assistants, Charles F. Willard and Charles Day, who later became very distinguished in aircraft engineering. Martin quickly took his place as a prominent and busy plane builder as well as a fine and exciting exhibition performer.

In the decades to follow, Glenn L. Martin's progress as a leader in the aircraft industry was outstanding. Added to many other qualities, this pious-looking, conservative, but effective plane and factory builder had a knack for picking promising, highly competent assistants—so competent that after their excellent training with "fussy" Martin, they launched their own great careers. In addition to Willard and Day, two of Martin's most important assistants were Larry Bell and Donald Douglas, both of whom created great aircraft establishments bearing their names that are today of enormous importance. At the beginning of his work, Martin had recognized the Wright patent and had arranged permission for building his planes on licensing agreements.

As 1913 grew into 1914 the competition started to become vicious. By this time the public had had its fill of flying sensations, and gate receipts were beginning to fall off. The most active outfits, Curtiss, Wright, and newcomer Martin, were becoming increasingly aware of the military market. But appropriations from Congress were slim, and they did not absorb much of the available facilities that the burgeoning civilian exhibition frenzy had created. The drying up of this market was becoming increasingly ominous as 1914 began.

Arch Hoxsey, Wright flyer at the 1912 St. Louis Air Meet, caps the prewar exhibition era by giving a ride to the President of the United States, Theodore Roosevelt.

Congress was still unaware of what aviation was to mean in the coming year or so. The paltry $100,000 that had been voted in 1912 was grudgingly increased in 1913 to only $125,000, growing larger in 1914, when $250,000 was voted for each service. The 17 planes owned by both the services in 1912 grew to 40 in 1914. Too many mouths were trying to get food to live on from the same basket. There simply was not enough, and everybody was about to go broke.

During 1914 the budding U.S. air industry had built about 400 planes of all types. Of these, however, only 6 new ones were for the Army and 4 for the Navy. Scores of others were complete flops, or merely freaks. Dozens of new companies were coming into existence, making matters even worse. Many were still hypnotized by the allure of the exhibition field, the fat prize offers, the sensational headlines. To these newcomers, the Wright patent was scoffed at, unlikely to be upheld . . . too broad.

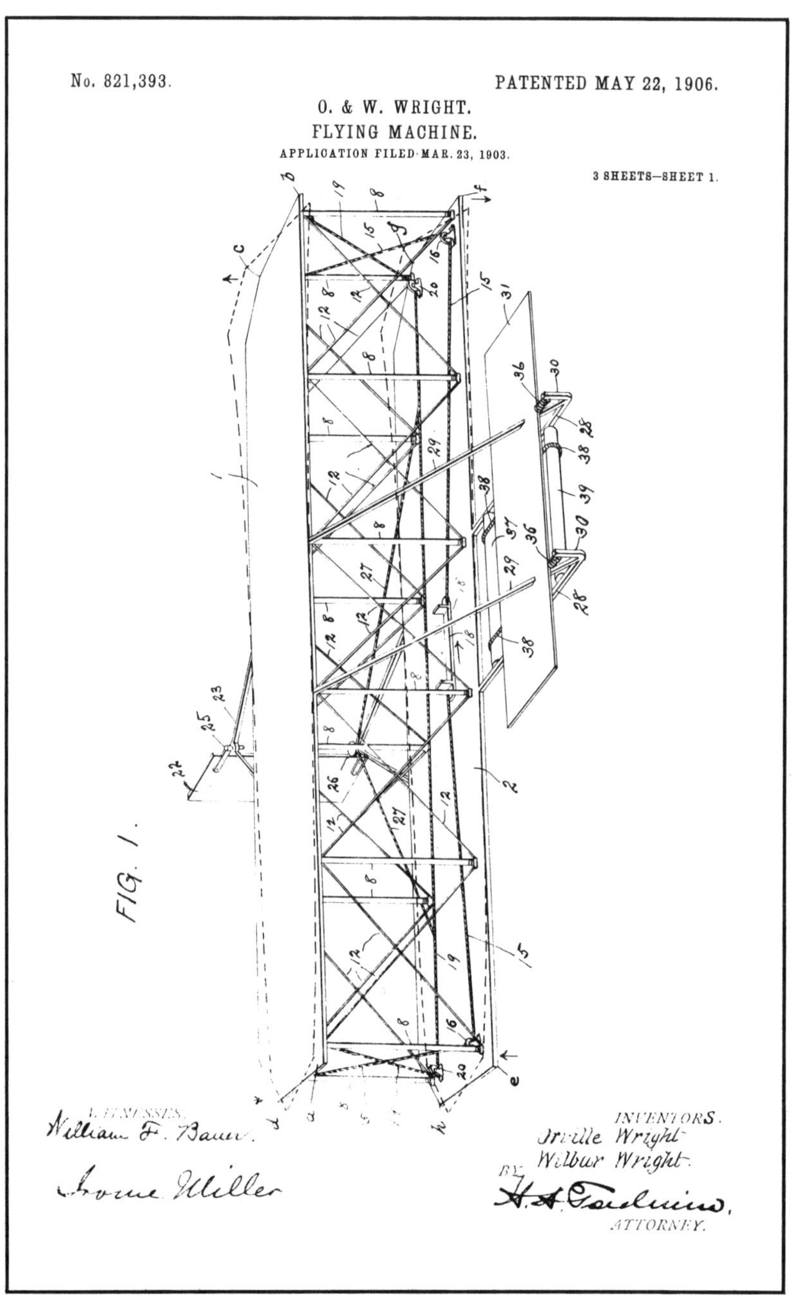

The first page of the Wright patent.

U.S. Patent Office

3 Monopoly in the Offing

TO MAKE MATTERS still worse, a Sword of Damocles hung over the struggling aircraft builders of the U.S. It fell on their heads very suddenly, although the experienced ones knew it could come sooner or later.

The Wright patent.

It happened January 13, 1914, with these words: "We are in full accord with the reasoning by which Judges Hazel and Hand reached the conclusions that the patent in suit is a valid one, that the patentees may fairly be considered pioneers in the practical art of flying . . . and that the claims should have a liberal interpretation." (The judges named had heard the earlier 1910 suits brought to enjoin Paulhan and Farman, foreign aviators, as well as Curtiss, from flying for profit in the United States.)

So read the final decision of the U. S. Circuit Court of Appeals in the case of the Wright Company, complainant, against the Herring-Curtiss Company and against Glenn H. Curtiss personally. This court action had been dragging on for almost five years. The defendants had used every resource of delay, appeal, postponement, drawn-out witness presentations, etc.

The decision seemed a final one. It was generally held unlikely that the Supreme Court would hear it further.

The air people woke up in January 1914, therefore, to the puzzling problem, "What will the Wright Company do? Will a system of reasonable royalties be worked out, or will they start to close out their competition in a field in which they have a fully legal right to build a monopoly?" The telephone company and many other patent-based monopoly industries like Gillette safety razors, Mergenthaler Linotype machines, and McCormick reapers showed how it could be done.

The business of the Dayton brothers had changed and grown considerably from its early beginnings. The bicycle-shop profits, with a little additional help from "Schwesterchen" Katherine Wright's schoolteacher's salary, had seen them through the early days of glider building and the first powered plane. Then had come some opportune patent payments, like the one paid by Morgan when the proposed French contract of 1906 was forfeited. So the Wrights had managed to scrimp along until July 1909, when the Army contract payment put them in fine shape. Further help had come from Russell and Fred Alger of Detroit and Robert Collier of New York, particular friends of the Wrights, who had ordered planes.

While Wilbur was in New York in 1909 at the Hudson Fulton Celebration, he had ample opportunity through August Belmont to meet many financially prominent men. Several promoters approached them, notably Clinton Peterkin and Andrew Freedman. There are many stories of how and with what discerning judgment Wilbur became identified with a group of the most prominent Wall Street capitalists. They were much impressed by this taciturn, closemouthed, but polite man. Delancy Nicoll, a leading corporation lawyer, helped greatly in the final organization of the first corporate outfit called The Wright Company. Its roster of directors and stockholders reads like a Blue Book of its day. Included were millionaires Cornelius Vanderbilt, August Belmont, Howard Gould, Thomas F. Ryan, E. J. Berwind, Robert J. Collier,

Fred and Russell Alger, Mortimer F. Plant, and Theodore P. Shonts.

The capital stock was a paid-in-cash proposition of $200,000 as a starter, later raised to $1,000,000 capital. The new company acquired all rights to the patents; the brothers received cash as well as stock; a 10 percent royalty was to be paid them on all planes sold. More than that, the company would bear the expense of prosecuting patent infringers. A pretty good deal for a "shy" inventor, reputed to talk so little. "Parrots talk . . . don't fly." Shy and modest the Wrights were, until Wilbur hit Wall Street. Then their tremendous success—completing the Army contract, making deals on the patents in France and Germany, selling a machine to Italy, and winning so much exhibition money—all added up to a convincing story that Wilbur, in his laconic way, could and did make appealing and inspiring to these tough business geniuses.

The generally accepted legend that Wilbur was so sparing with words is belied by this eloquent passage, verbatim, from his testimony in one of the patent suits, when he was describing rough air and curls of smoke.

"And yet it is in such capricious, willful, spasmodic and withal powerful a medium as this, that our Wright flying machine rides and speeds away, with man or men aboard, like a veritable living albatross. It plants itself on the incorrigible air and rides upon its very incorrigibility."

Seven months earlier, Curtiss had made his first corporate move, already noted, when the Herring-Curtiss Company was started with millionaire Courtlandt Field Bishop, one of the early balloon and Aero Club aficionados. But it was never as serious a business move, with real cash involved, such as the Wright undertaking.

Wilbur Wright was named president of the new company, and handsome offices were set up in New York at 527 Fifth Avenue. In a few months a new factory was being built in Dayton and a first-class organization lined up. In New York, Alpheus Barnes, a typical Wall Street cigar-smoking executive

The original Wright Company plant at Dayton, Ohio.

office manager, was installed as the secretary and treasurer of the company. In Dayton, at the new plant, Frank Russell, on the recommendation of the Algers from Detroit, was installed as factory manager. The production plan they worked out called for the delivery of about four planes a month, which was in excess of Curtiss capacity at that time, or that of any plant in Europe.

As we have seen, the exhibition business in 1910 had begun to assume serious proportions. Roy Knabenshue, already an experienced aeronautical exhibition, circus, and fair promoter, as well as a dirigible airship pilot, was placed in charge of this part of the activities of the Wrights. It was a position that he carried to a financial success undreamed of when it all began. The profit-seeking Wall Street members of the Wright board joined with the brothers in deciding to get all they could, and began a series of lawsuits to close paid exhibitions by others and the winning of prize money by competitors. Injunctions were applied for against Louis Paulhan and Henri Farman

Grover Loening and Orville Wright—Dayton, Ohio, 1913.

from France, who were about to give big shows at Sheepshead Bay Racetrack near New York. The injunctions were granted and the money prizes enjoined.

Curtiss, too, was tackled by a suit effectively to make him desist from any activity in which he would earn money by exploiting his infringing product. This was the lawsuit that several years later was decided by the U. S. Circuit Court of Appeals in Buffalo, New York, and it was this thunderbolt that the Wall Street group backing the Wrights had been waiting for so hopefully. When the suit was decided in the Wrights' favor, they rolled up their sleeves to get to work and build a great new protected industry. That sweet word . . . *monopoly* . . . and a legal one, was in the air.

In July 1913, six months before the final Buffalo decision was announced, I reported for duty at the Dayton factory, newly hired as Orville's assistant and presently to succeed Frank Russell as manager. Before leaving New York, I met "Al" Barnes at his office. He briefed me about a lot of things relating to the company.

"Grover, let me tell you something," he began, in a confidential tone, as if letting me in on some inside gossip. I noticed the use of my first name. He was so much older and more formidable-looking that it took me time to respond on the same level. "The Wrights are funny people. Wilbur died of typhoid fever in May 1912, and ever since Orville succeeded him as president, we really have no boss. He takes forever to make a decision . . . nothing like the quick-acting, quicker-thinking Wilbur. Maybe the breakup of the team has had a bad effect."

It was evident that the older brother and the one who had originally done the dealings with this "downtown" group was Al's hero, his favorite, and that he grieved at Wilbur's untimely death.

In a patronizing, somewhat fatherly way, Barnes put one hand on my knee, holding his ever-present cigar in the other. "You and I are New Yorkers, and we don't think like these Ohio hicks. The interest of everyone in this company is to grow and expand and make a great big thing out of this magnificent opportunity. You know our board and their influence and importance. As soon as we get our final patent decision"—he hesitated, blew smoke at the ceiling—"watch for the fireworks!"

Barnes continued describing the handsome new factory that had been built, and how Orville had disagreements with Russell, who finally had resigned. No doubt through Barnes' mind passed the thought, *If this kid gets the slant that his job is not too secure with Orv unless he also has the support of my office and the board in New York, we may be able to use him to spy out Orv's strange tactics and really find out where we are headed.* He continued to picture the future, in particular how impressed all those important directors would be with me if I could induce Orville to get out some newer and more modern designs than the *Model B* then in production. "Give some thought to two fields that seem to be growing so quickly." Barnes reached for some photos. "Look how Curtiss has gotten way ahead of us with his hydroairplane flying off the water for the Navy." He puffed his cigar and went on. "People in Europe seem to be concentrating on the tractor type of plane, with the propeller in front and the body enclosed." Al, showing me more new pictures, succeeded in firing my imagination and stirring up a rapprochement that lasted for some time. There was considerable letter writing between us. Unknowingly, I probably had become his spy.

When I got to Dayton, another aspect of this inside organization came out. It was soon made clear that Barnes was not very high in Orville's esteem, nor did he have much influence in the factory's business operations. In fact, it appeared that Orville was even annoyed by Barnes, and wondered what Wilbur had seen in him. Reports on expenditures had to be sent every week to the New York office, and Orville made it clear that he considered this a meaningless nuisance, to be followed patiently to satisfy the group in Wall Street.

In his direct and crisp manner he said, "They don't really know how this airplane business should be run, and they never will. They still apply old manufacturing rules and customs to something that is so different," and he shook his head as if it were hopeless to expect otherwise. It was then that I realized how much Orville needed Wilbur, and that the success of the team had perhaps run its course.

Letters would arrive needing prompt answers. They would be relayed to Orville's office on West Third Street, some two miles from the factory. He held forth there with his faithful secretary, Mabel Beck. It soon was evident that she, too, did not rate Barnes very high. Some of these letters would not be answered for weeks, to a newcomer a shocking example of poor organization. When reminded of this, Mr. Wright would answer, "Oh, I have been so busy on the research I am doing, these matters will just have to wait." So I started answering some of them myself, at least with an acknowledgment. I expected to be fired . . . but no, he seemed relieved.

Every time a situation arose that required the presence of the president of the Wright Company at a hearing or conference or a technical meeting. Orville would voice to me his annoyance at the thought of leaving Dayton. Then one day he told me, "They don't seem to realize that my sciatica from the Fort Myer accident is still very bothersome." He twitched his hips in emphasis. "It is very painful for me to ride a train or stand up for too long a time." This was kept in the strictest confidence, as he wanted it to be. But it revealed many things to me. The most important man in the airplane business in the U. S. was sick and ailing, and few knew it. Hence his preference for staying at his Third Street office so near his home; the extra soft springing that he had installed on his Franklin air-cooled car, which rode like a baby carriage; the occasional agonized grimaces, obviously from a sharp spasm. Viewed from this distance, many of his vagaries and indecisions doubtless were due to the private suffering he so courageously hid from the world. And since Wilbur's death, many noted how Orville had changed, and seemed somewhat lost.

As the months went by I learned that he was indeed a great genius, but a troubled one. He brooded much on the injustice of the rising competition that was robbing him of the fruits of invention. On this subject he would talk for hours. I realized how vital for the coming air industry's growth would be his reactions and decisions. And how miserable he was at the prospect of facing it all alone.

An interesting angle of his thinking was revealed one day when a discussion was held on the then-new vogue of tractor types, with engine and propeller in front. Orville said, "This type is really an invention of the French, and we should not be copying it just to keep up. There must be better reasons than that." He picked up some foreign magazines, glanced at them.

Orville Wright tests the *Model G* flying boat on the narrow Miami River.

He continued, "Since the chief use of airplanes for the military will be observation, how can you justify putting the pilot behind so much engine-propeller interference, spoiling his view?" He found and pointed at a picture of a tractor type. "Its only real merit is that the plane can go a little faster." Having convinced himself, he threw the magazines down on the table. For several years the Wright Company did not move in the direction of this all-around-better form of aircraft, the tractor-type plane that was to be proved so correct in the coming years. It was evident, anyhow, that copying someone else was not in Orville's makeup. He would never have approved of the short-hull flying boat, the Wright *Model G,* developed in early 1914 and sold to the Navy and several individuals, if its appearance had not been so totally different from the Curtiss *F* boat that was sweeping the field. Years later the Navy-Curtiss

NC-4, first across the Atlantic, was of the short-hull type.

Whenever an occasion arose involving a flight test, Orville was a different man—keen, quick, careful, and obviously *one* with the machine. It was always a thrill to see him get to work in the domain of the air that he ruled with such a sure, certain and smooth hand. There was no indecision then, no hesitating, no procrastinating. The master was on the job! And the sciatica had given way to real joy. On such occasions every discerning person could see by comparison how he loathed business and its boring duties. Yet his influence and prestige put him in the leading position to guide the air industry's growth. The climax of his flying pleasure in those years occurred when he was demonstrating his automatic stabilizing system. This was one of several research projects that he was conducting in secret, concealed even from his factory staff. None of us were allowed access to this until the time came when I had arranged for a committee from the Aero Club to witness his flights for the possible award of the Collier Trophy for which we had promoted his candidacy. The flights in midwinter winds were a triumph. He won the trophy. This meant much to the Wright directors and Barnes, as an evidence of active advancement. Curtiss had won this trophy two years running. Bob Collier, who had donated it, was particularly pleased.

At the very beginning of 1914, the Navy had moved its base of air operations from Annapolis, Maryland, to the revived old Navy establishment at Pensacola, Florida. The Navy invited representatives from the major aircraft companies as guests to take part in this occasion. Mr. Wright, owing to his dislike of traveling, sent me.

While I was away, on this duty, the Buffalo decision upholding the Wrights on the patent was announced. The news had reached Pensacola by wire, and it was uncomfortable for me with the other aircraft people. I didn't know how to answer their questions, and their teasing was annoying. What were we in for? I couldn't figure it out. I sensed definite hostility taking root in others in the industry.

Then from Al Barnes came a letter, special delivery, to Pensacola:

Mr. Grover Loening
c/o USS Mississippi
Pensacola, Florida

My dear Grover:

No doubt you have read or heard of the decision of the court in our favor. I enclose a copy of the decision so that you can see for yourself it is quite true.

Our Company will now control the manufacture and sale of machines in the United States absolutely.

I am off for Dayton Sunday and look forward to a very pleasant visit there as I feel sure things will now begin to hum.

Yours sincerely,
Alpheus F. Barnes

Walking into the office at the plant, on my return from this Navy trip, I found Al Barnes comfortably installed at my desk. I was taken aback . . . was I fired? He assured me that I was not, as he got up to shake hands and moved himself and his papers over to a new table that he had had installed.

We were alone in the office conversing, Barnes with his lit cigar, when in walked Orville. Hardly noticing me, he turned to Barnes with a rather hurt look, and politely said, "Sorry that I am so bothered by this smoke, Mr. Barnes, but Wil and I were never at all able to abide the habit." He coughed slightly (I thought it was forced) and turned to me. "I hope you're not going to take it up." Admonishingly said, with a slight threat. Then, "If you could come to the Third Street office this afternoon, you can report on the Navy visit." This was said in a clipped tone, which distinctly intimated that Barnes need not be let in on any of it.

I got the message all right. Life from now on was to be a

tight-rope-walking act of staying friends with Barnes without being fired by Orville.

One afternoon a few days later, when pressing factory matters had been taken care of, Barnes and I relaxed into a reviewing mood. "These Dayton Ohio hicks," said Barnes, "aren't they something to write home about? . . . It's not the way they dress or live nearly so much as the way they think." It crossed my mind . . . *they think well enough to invent airplanes, and self-starters, and cash registers and many other things that are making this town boom like crazy*. Barnes went on. "You know how our people in New York operate. You're close enough through your family to the Vanderbilt-Belmont-Collier group to understand why our board members are worried about Orville carrying out the policies that these men risked their money to put

Smithsonian's National Air and Space Museum

While the Wright Company was worrying about patents, Curtiss was busy pioneering the hydroairplane. This photo shows the first successful seaplane, with Curtiss testing it in 1911, two years ahead of the Wright flying boat effort. Note the ailerons between the wings designed to bypass the Wright patent.

over." I knew what he meant . . . knew that the Wall Street contingent would take monetary risks mainly if they saw a big killing in the offing. To the Wright directors, Orville, unlike his late, more enterprising brother, was showing signs of being an apple-cart upsetter. That was why Barnes had been sent to Dayton. Al himself said, "What the Wright Company does in the next few months, or even weeks, will influence the entire future of this little industry. It can be a damn sight bigger than any of these dumb Ohio clucks can even imagine."

In our many discussions Al brought out some potent reasons in favor of a monopoly. Accidents, with their depressing effect on the public, would be fewer by cutting out the "cheap-skate" experimenter with his unscientifically built plane. The attraction and glamor of the flying "enthusiast" was aviation's own worst enemy. Too many people came into the game with no hope of doing anything more than bankrupting their backers and stealing market growth from the competent pioneers.

One big, rich company with a large enough market to afford it could set up a fine research and development establishment, as the telephone monopoly was doing with its Western Electric Company. "The flying machine business," said Barnes, "can still be caught and set up on a patent monopoly basis; but there's no time to lose."

But the time was being lost. The next move was to enter suit against a newly organized unit, the Curtiss Aeroplane Company. It had been organized by Curtiss during the Wrights' former litigation with the old and by now defunct Herring-Curtiss outfit; more outwitting of the Wrights by the smart Curtiss rivals. The January 1914 order from the U.S. Court of Appeals had enjoined this older company, and Curtiss personally, from "making, using, selling, or exhibiting flying machines, permanently." Now they had slid out from under by creating this new company. A combination of delaying tactics by Curtiss, added to Mr. Wright's hesitancy in answering letters and signing papers, meant that it was not until November 1914 that this highly important suit got before the court. World War I, which was to have such a vital effect on this patent matter, had already started.

These delays and dilatory ways began to unnerve the Wright directors. Likewise, they began to lose Orville's loyalty and cooperation. There were disagreeable flareups in the office between Barnes and Orville, making things uncomfortable and strained. It was enough for Al faintly to suggest that something be done for Orville to place an emphatic "no" on it.

The situation at the office began to get intolerable. The friction between Al and Mr. Wright had to reach a climax. When Orville was not there, Al and I would read about Curtiss winning another prize or trophy and fume silently. He would tell me again and again what a great guy Wilbur had been in comparison, and on the few times that I had talked to Wilbur, and from the treasured letters that he had written me when I was a student, I could but agree with him.

When the blowup came I was not there, having resigned to accept the position of the first Aeronautical Engineer of the U.S. Army, stationed at the Signal Corps Flying School at San Diego, California. But I learned about it in letters from Barnes and some of my former staff at Dayton, as well as from the aircraft press.

Apparently, the directors were upset at the way they would write letters to Mr. Wright and never get an answer. Also, they realized that under his management the progress of the company would not be as they wanted it. Mr. Wright did not seem to mind these reactions. They fitted his plans! After about July 1914, he began to buy up the stockholdings of first one director, then another. Finally, he had bought them all out except Bob Collier, who was a close and loyal friend of his. Barnes was of course dismissed as soon as Mr. Wright could do it. No more hard feelings, the party was over.

Importantly for the future of the air industry, the monopoly threat was much weakened.

Orville Wright now owned his company and did not have to defer to anyone—didn't have to answer letters or attend meetings. He could now retire from all the business headaches that Wilbur had gotten him into, which is exactly what he did. After a few months, in 1915, a very different New York syndicate, more patent license-minded, headed by William Boyce Thompson, the great mining tycoon, and Frank Manville, president of the Johns-Manville Company, made a satisfactory offer and Orville accepted. The offer netted him a huge profit.

Perhaps not so "dumb" after all, these "Ohio hicks"!

Smithsonian's National Air and Space Museum

The Army Signal Corps Aviation Section Flying School at San Diego, California, scene of the greatest U.S. aviation activity starting in 1913. Here was introduced the Martin *TT* training plane of tractor type (above), which was to play such an important role in the safety of our air operations.

4 The War's Shadow Appears

THE MOST IMPORTANT developments for American aviation's future in the years 1913 to 1915 took place in or around North Island at San Diego, California. There the Army established its first serious aviation school. Curtiss, too, had by then based his pioneer hydroairplane work there. He made the first flight off the waters in America there in 1911, and he continued to carry on experiments at and near North Island, and conducted his own school there. The year-round good flying weather expedited progress, and the whole atmosphere of this region invited air development.

In April 1914, Congress had appropriated the much larger sum of $250,000 for Army flying, almost as much for the Navy. By July Congress had passed a bill establishing the new Aviation Section of the Army Signal Corps in the Army as a separate unit.

In 1913 the Army had ended the year with 17 planes, 22 officers, 90 enlisted men. Less than a year later it had grown to an authorization of 60 officers and 200 men, with about 30 planes delivered or on order. All these and more were needed because the casualty rate was shocking. In the course of the

1909-13 years, out of a group of 14 officers taking flying training, 9 had been killed. The equipment consisted mostly of Wright pushers, *Model B* and a newer *Model C*, plus a few Curtiss single-propeller pushers. The training had been done by a few officers who had been through the Wright or Curtiss schools.

There was a great outcry in the press, leading to Congressional hearings about the tragic series of fatal accidents. A measure of blame was placed on the practice of assigning the few trained Army pilots like Lieutenants Tommy Milling, Harry Arnold, Roy Kirtland and others to teach new pupils in addition to their own duties in military operations. To improve this condition as well as to allay criticism, the head of the Aviation Section, Colonel Samuel Reber, introduced the new policy of employing civilian experts in positions of flying instructors and aeronautical engineers to take charge of training, maintenance, repair, teaching, and other duties.

When the civilians, including myself, were settled at the San Diego school and our authority determined, the first thing we recommended and followed through on was to condemn all pusher-type planes as unsafe and unsuitable for the training of flying students—as indeed they were. Many were the photographs attesting to the way engines at their back had fallen on and crushed the bodies of the pilots of these impractical aircraft.

Then the fun began of finding proper new planes to fill the vacuum! It was the consensus of the school personnel that it would have to be a tractor type. The quickest action was obtained from Glenn Martin of Los Angeles. He had a two-seat, land-type tractor biplane that he had started to use in exhibitions but had developed with training in mind. He had also mounted it on floats. After a group of us, headed by Lieutenant Milling, conferred with him at his plant, Martin agreed to bring his plane down to San Diego and demonstrate it. As soon as he appeared with the sleek, well-built plane, his first order from the U. S. Government was assured him. The new craft made an immediate hit in every way, including its use of a new 8-cylinder Curtiss O engine. This marked the start of the huge military aircraft business that Martin was to build up in the ensuing decades. The Martin *TT*, as it was called, became the first successful aircraft on which really safe training could be accomplished. As a result of this initial move by the Army, training fatalities fell almost to nothing compared with the tragedies of the years before. That fatality rate of 9 out of 14 aviation pilots was reduced to 1 out of 29!

By the end of 1914 the attention of the aircraft industry was riveted on the market opening up for the training of aviators. World War I had started, and although the use of aircraft was at first limited and uncertain, observation flying came rapidly into use, and this meant that aviators had to be trained in a hurry. The aircraft companies then looked to San Diego's North Island activities with much greater interest than was being given to the dying and too competitive exhibition business. They also kept an eye on what was going on in Europe in the hesitant and limited application of aircraft to war use. Garros had not yet mounted his first gun on his monoplane; Fokker had not yet synchronized the firing of bullets through the propeller. Pusher planes, with the engine behind the pilot, were still preferred for reconnaisance. A few more months were to change all that.

The North Island wave for tractor biplane procurement rose to new intensity as Burgess (by then a Wright licensee), Curtiss, and others plunged in with Martin to fill the gap created by abandonment of the old pushers.

Sales teams began to appear at the Army school. The Curtiss group, headed by Ray Morris, a fine test pilot and salesman, would explain confidentially why the Martin *TT* was so dangerous and deficient, only to have Martin himself, with his smooth talking, backed up by his virtuoso flying, make monkeys of the Curtiss crowd. Armed with know-how from their technical civilian aides, including Oscar Brindley, George Hallett, and myself, the young Army aviators were not very

The Signal Corps tractor, the first development project of the Experimental and Repair Division of the Army School (which later grew into the Engineering Division). This plane, a modified Burgess, incorporated trailing edge ailerons instead of warping, and had a simple two-wheel landing gear, later to become widely used. Many records were made with this plane.

gullible. Naturally they were not averse to carrying on the endless discussions into the night if the free drinks held out, and if the social angles were attractive enough. Sound progress in design and procurement in this period of airplane development was evidenced by the intelligent, hard-bitten attitude the Army aviators had acquired from their technical teachers. Many of the young West Point lieutenants, like Byron Q. Jones, Harold Martin, and Virginius Clark, took so readily to acquiring technical proficiency that they became competent engineers in their own right, and subsequently very expert inspectors at factories. In later years, their expertise meant much in insuring the high quality of American aircraft products. Clark followed me as Chief Engineer of the Aviation Section.

Late in 1914 this feverish activity crystalized into a competition held to determine the best tractor biplane for training, with a large order as the prize. This was well organized with Benny Foulois (by then a major) as the head of the contest board. Glenn Martin, Starling Burgess, and lesser known builders vied with Curtiss for acceptance. Curtiss had entered two planes, the *Model J,* which landed too fast and was tricky because of a too narrow landing gear, and the *Model N,* the fastest entry. But the *N* was longitudinally unstable, owing to faulty balance and angle of incidence setting. Martin ran off with the honors in this first round.

Histories of aviation seldom mention this highly important period in the growth and maturation of the aircraft manufacturing field; chiefly because under Colonel Reber and Major Foulois, the policy of "no publicity" was rigorously followed. The whole atmosphere of this contest was aimed professionally at the acquisition of a better training machine, and not at personal acclaim for any individual. A rare instance in air history!

Where was the great Wright Company in all of this competition? Not a sign of Orville until much later. Milling and I had often written him. Few letters were answered, and he took no interest in the tractor types, only in the large twin-propeller engine in front of the *Model F* that he was then completing. I thought that he probably had taken my condemnation of his old pushers as evidence of disloyalty. A feeling that he would never forgive me lasted for many years until, long after the war, I received an autographed copy of Fred Kelly's excellent book, *The Wright Brothers,* with the following inscription:

> To Grover C. Loening,
> with kind remembrances and affectionate regards,
> Orville Wright.

During this period I also came to know Glenn Curtiss much better, socially as well as professionally, and found him a dynamic force and keen planner for his company's growth and for aviation's future in general. The difference between Curtiss and Orville Wright in manner and mental process was most evident when technical questions were raised. If Curtiss were asked, "What is the area of your rudder control surface?" he would very likely reply, "I don't know . . . but if it isn't big enough the 'boys' will fix it." To the same kind of question, Wright would reply by referring to the little notebook that he always carried and telling you the exact area and dimensions.

Essentially, Curtiss was a promoter with vision; Wright was an engineer and a scientist.

The rivalry that had been so acute and often bitter between the Wright and Curtiss fliers in the exhibition business carried over for a while into the Army fliers' activities. But soon this died out when Glenn Martin began to take the orders away from both of the older outfits.

Every week more and more news filtered through on how the planes were being used in the growing war at the French front. Military adjuncts to flying appeared at the North Island fields, often secretly.

The French, faced by a hostile and threatening Germany, were constantly war-minded and were the first nation to steer their aviation development to its possible use in war. Accordingly, industry and the French Government offered many prizes at this time for developments that could strengthen their warplane potential. The first item that commanded attention was a prize for bomb dropping, offered in the form of the Michelin prize for accuracy. It was won in 1912 by American Army Lt. Riley Scott against many contestants from several nations. He had tried to interest Washington in his bombsight but got nowhere until he went abroad and won this prize. After it had been disclosed, our Army did its usual tardy act and invited Scott to bring his device to North Island, where facilities were accorded him to continue with his development. However, "secrecy" was to surround his work, the European disclosure notwithstanding. Other new military projects were under test at the San Diego field, and the Aviation Section Signal Corps School became quite a center for military development as well as for training.

It was in these years 1914 to 1916 the First Aero Squadron, our pioneer military unit, was organized and grew to new stature. At its start there were 16 officers, 77 enlisted men and 8 planes. Its chief activity soon was with the punitive expedition to Mexico to check Pancho Villa's revolutionary raids and the numerous border incidents that resulted from them. Planes became needed and, hopefully, might be useful for observation and scouting. A good deal of material for the border operations then centering on El Paso, Texas, was prepared or worked on at the North Island shops. One of these, an outstanding success, was a mobile field machine shop for repairs and maintenance of planes and motors. This was devised and built by engineer George Hallett.

Capt. Charles DeF. Chandler of the Aviation Section had already mounted a Lewis machine gun on the front of a Wright plane and fired it, but received neither enthusiasm nor encouragement from the rest of the Army. As early as 1912, the aviators faced scorn, hostility and even interference from other branches that could not visualize or tolerate this newfangled air arm as having any military value.

As for radio aboard aircraft—called "wireless" at that time—several steps had been taken in the United States. One of the earliest was the association of Elmo Pickerill with Dr. Lee De Forest, the wireless pioneer, and with the Marconi Company. Late in 1910 Pickerel had visited Orville Wright, who had given him flying lessons. He managed at that early date to make air-to-ground contact in the neighborhood of New York and Long Island. At about this time, J. A. D. McCurdy in his Curtiss biplane also succeeded in establishing some radio contact.

This door was opened wider in November 1912. Fort Riley, Kansas, had been the scene of artillery maneuvers in which Lt. H. H. Arnold (later Gen. "Hap" Arnold, Air Chief in World War II) sent messages to the ground, noting the accuracy of gunfire. The work on communications continued at San Diego.

Two important pieces of equipment for the safety of aviators had not yet received any serious attention at the Army school. One was the parachute, then considered merely a circus or fair stunt. The other equally vital oversight was safety belts. Foulois had one made especially for him in 1910, but it is inconceivable today that with the emphasis on safety of that time, they were not mandatory. But one type was developed by Lieutenant Milling, and North Island soon provided belts for all.

While the Army was carrying on its training and other activities at San Diego, the Navy was developing its flying at Pensacola, Florida, where its school, established early in 1914, was growing rapidly. The aircraft industry watched this Naval source of business, with an eye to filling the needs of this other service. In effect the Navy thus was another customer, even though both it and the Army were part of the U.S. Government. Without question the military requirements of the two services were distinct, but in training of student aviators in the primary classes, there was little difference. Fortunately for the industry, however, the Navy did not think so, and Navy procurement proceeded independently from the outset. This policy has persisted through the years and has been a boon to the aircraft industry although rarely admitted and officially glossed over. The game the industry played through the years with these two customers was hidden to any but wise eyes. But the repeated playing off of one customer against the other was practiced to the advantage not only of the manufacturers but of the services too. For one thing, American procurement created a keen rivalry for the best in aircraft, and also a sparkling competition in making records and in winning races. This was one outstanding difference between the uniquely American procurement system and the manner in which the nations of Europe developed their systems and organizations. Through the years, this rivalry has been found to be an effective reason for our superiority in competition with European nations on any particular phase of aviation. Many a new design that had merit was turned down by the Army for invalid reasons. These designs then were brought frequently to the Navy and were received with interest and encouragement, sometimes with orders. The Navy, too, turned down promising proposals for a new type of plane for reasons of unwarranted doubt or failure to meet preformed prejudices; these then went to the Army and found no such objections.

Smithsonian's National Air and Space Museum

Developed through early models, the final engine for training in 1915 to 1919 was the Curtiss 8-cylinder 90-horsepower OX-5, weighing 376 pounds.

There was then, as now, enormous merit for our aviation progress in having two customers with different points of view. Several important American aircraft and engine designs of great value would have died on the drawing board but for this procurement setup. For example, when the histories of the start of and subsequent development of the Wright Whirlwind and the Pratt & Whitney Wasp radial air-cooled engines are examined, it becomes evident that the lack of interest of the Army at that time in radial air-cooled engines of any make would have checked progress in this immensely important area. But the Navy stepped in with its different and more enlightened point of view, and ordered into production the two most successful motors of that day—first the Whirlwind and then the Wasp. Their descendants are still widely used all over the world, almost forty years later! There was a short period during World War II when General Henry H. Arnold's requirement that all fighter planes were to have radial air-cooled engines had to give way to using Rolls and Allison water-cooled engines in the *Mustang P-51* fighter. This was in order to get the range and speed needed to accompany *B-17* bombers.

When the Navy's Pensacola school was in high gear in 1914 and 1915, it had started using a few Curtiss and Wright push-

Curtiss Aeroplane Company photo of F flying boat used for training. Ray Morris tests the pilot seat. Standing, Beckwith Havens, famous exhibition flyer.

ers mounted on floats. These were replaced rapidly by the Curtiss flying boat *Model F's* as soon as this excellent new type could be procured from the Hammondsport factory. The *F* boat was still dangerous, however, because the motor was placed over the head of the aviator, and in a hard crash it could have the same deadly effect that the Army had experienced with their early pusher types. Army aviation personnel wondered about this and argued much with their Navy confreres, whose answer, somewhat facetious but with a modicum of sense, was that the water was so much softer to strike than hard ground as to reduce this danger. This was proven true in several instances. Nevertheless, when 1915 was drawing to its close, the Navy also acquired the "tractor complex" and proceeded to reequip with Curtiss *JN*-class training planes on floats, again with a notable decrease in fatal accidents during training. Other tractors were developed for Navy training, among them the *Sturtevant* designed by Loening. A year or so later, excellent biplane tractors were built by Boeing and

Aeromarine. The flying boat remained a favorite for military action, and was used in the Mexican-Huerta trouble of 1914 at Vera Cruz, when Lt. E. O. McDonnell (the famous Eddie McDonnell, later an admiral) made a brilliant landing attack on the beach, under fire, to establish a flying boat base, a feat for which he genuinely deserved his Congressional Medal of Honor.

After August 1914, all aviation minds were watching carefully to learn how planes would be used in World War I. The start of war operations was slow and hesitant at the front. The German Army had started on a fast advance into French territory, gravely threatening the British Army sector. The electrifying news came that the Royal Flying Corps (R.F.C.) (established only a year before) was at that front and in action. The pilots in the observation planes had discovered a German threat just in time to allow the British command to change dispositions, and not only to save itself from a disaster but also to inflict serious enough damage at Mons to the German plan of attack to cause the enemy to give up that phase. Air power had won its first signal victory, and there was a flush of triumph in the eyes of all aviation people. This British application of aircraft at the Battle of Mons was all the more remarkable because the R.F.C., with only 1,800 men and 200 officers, had so few active planes when the war started. It was disclosed in the House of Commons in June 1914 that the British Army had a total of only 176 planes, 70 of which were under repair. The War Office Secretary stated further, "It would not be in the public interest to state how many were fitted with wireless telegraph or photographic apparatus." At the opening of hostilities, France was the strongest nation in flying machines, with 1,500 on active service, while Germany had about 1,000. But the Germans also had 40 dirigible balloons, chiefly Zeppelins, with which they fully intended to bomb London. Their planes did not yet have the range or carrying capacity for such an operation.

The number of American Army and Navy planes at that time

totaled about 80 ready for some service but limited largely to training. However, the war was having its effect on appropriations. Due to the submarine menace, the Navy received prime attention from Congress, with $1,000,000 voted for aviation, including dirigibles as well as flying boats. The Army by early 1914 got a big increase to $300,000, which before the end of 1915 was suddenly increased to over $13,000,000. Congress had at last seen the light, and the beginning of our involvement in this distant war was becoming evident. By early 1917, things really were moving. The Navy's appropriation was up to $3,500,000 and the Army's to $14,280,000. The industry responded accordingly.

Other events in Washington made 1915 an exceedingly significant year in air history. At the Smithsonian Institution, the previously abandoned Langley laboratory where the original Langley *Aerodrome* had been developed was reactivated by Dr. Charles D. Walcott, head of the Smithsonian, and opened officially with Dr. A. F. Zahm as its director. At about the same time, government problems related to aeronautics piled up on the Administration and Congress, requiring expert handling for which Washington was not adequately staffed. Dr. Walcott and several industry leaders joined in, pushing through Congress a bill establishing something very new to our form of government—the National Advisory Committee for Aeronautics. This step was destined to give great prestige to the United States as well as an immense boost to the U. S. air industry. The first secretary of this organization was the loved and highly respected Dr. John F. Victory. He was to remain with it for the rest of his active life, a period of almost fifty years.

Just before the start of World War I in August, 1914, there had been significant happenings in Hammondsport at the Curtiss factory. Lord Northcliffe of the *London Daily Mail* (inspired to further encouragement of aviation) had offered a prize of $50,000 for the first aviator to cross the Atlantic in less than 72 hours. Rodman Wanamaker of New York, as a patriotic

Smithsonian's National Air and Space Museum

The National Advisory Committee for Aeronautics, April 23, 1915, at its first meeting. Seated, left to right: Dr. William F. Durand, Stanford University; Dr. S. W. Stratton, National Bureau of Standards; Brig. Gen. George P. Scriven, chief signal officer; Dr. Charles F. Marvin, Weather Bureau; Dr. Michael I. Pupin, Columbia University. Standing, left to right: Lt. Comdr. Holden C. Richardson, naval constructor; Dr. John F. Hayford, Northwestern University; Captain Mark L. Bristol, director of naval aeronautics; Lt. Col. Samuel Reber, Signal Corps.

move and a means of advertising his merchant empire, promptly decided to commission Curtiss to proceed with the design and construction of a large flying boat to win this prize. The new boat was to be called the *America*, and its test flights had already started when the outbreak of the war called it off. But Curtiss had made an important step in design by laying out a practical new model with two motors, one on each side of the hull—a type he was to follow up and develop further for the war. This project was taken over at once by the British under the leadership of Wanamaker's appointed pilot, Commander Porte of the British Navy. In short order, the *America*'s design went to England and became the famous *Felixtowe*

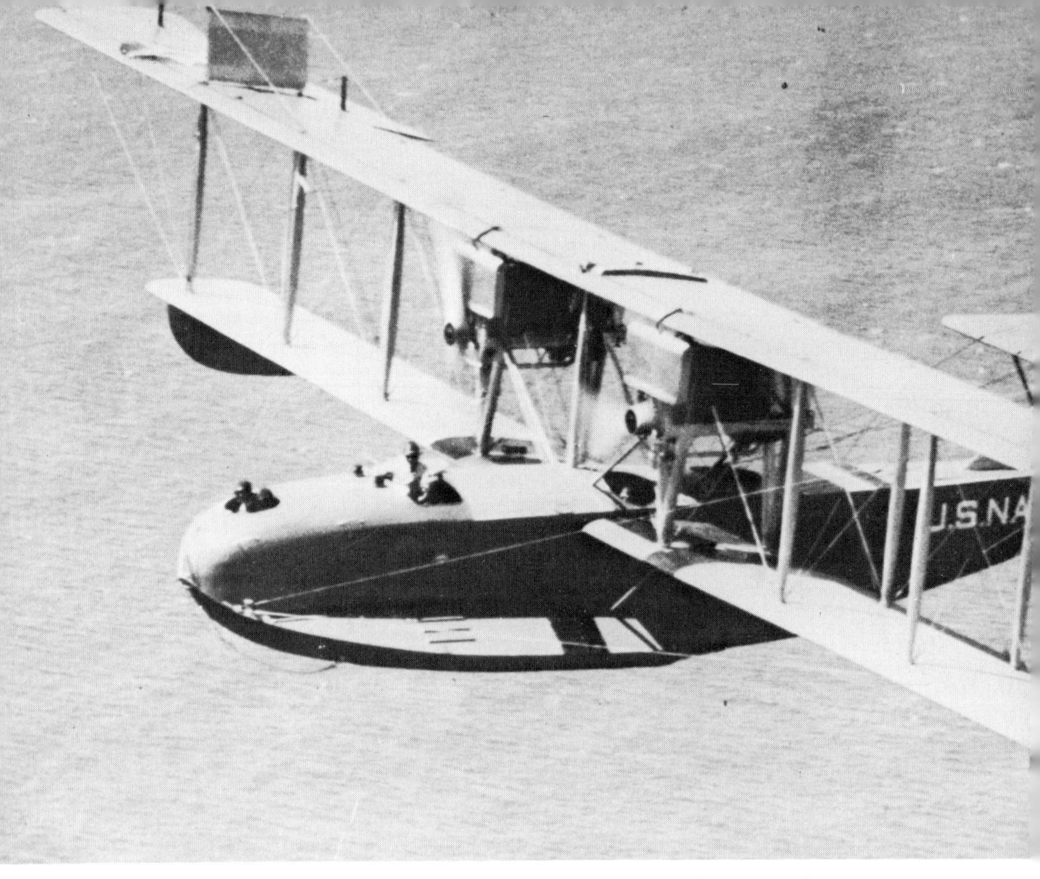

flying boat of the Royal Navy. Later the widely used U.S. Navy version was the *H16* boat with two 360-h.p. Liberty motors.

As 1916 dawned, activity in plane manufacturing grew rapidly. Curtiss had established a new factory in Buffalo. It was enlarged to take care of a huge order from Britain for the Curtiss training plane that had been developed from the Army's tests of the *J* type and the *N*. By combining the good features of both, this design ended up as the *JN*. After a few more model changes and a larger motor (the final 8-cylinder, 90 h.p. OX-5), this plane became the treasured, beloved and very widely used *JN-4*, the ubiquitous *Jennie* of decades to come. Soon the U.S. Army added to this British order more contracts for the same plane. Equipped with floats for the Navy, this type was named the *N-9*. Curtiss, then, began the first real production in our industry. The British and French placed other orders for planes and engines with American

Curtiss

The Curtiss *H-16* twin motor flying boat, used by the Navy in World War I.

producers, such as Burgess in Massachusetts. Some orders were for the Sturtevant 8-cylinder motor. Some foreign missions were already in the United States with tempting offers of orders for warplanes to take part in contests and to meet the needs of England, France, Italy, Russia, Argentina, and Japan. So the American industry in 1916 was expanding enormously; the U. S. designers and engineers were sharpening their pencils and oiling up their slide rules for a busy time ahead. As many as could do so sneaked abroad to get a line on what was needed for the war. The predominance of San Diego as the hot spot air of activity began to wane. Besides, it was rapidly becoming merely a big school and had been named Rockwell Field. In a few years the Army moved out and the Navy took over.

In its first ten years, aviation and its accompanying industry had grown from nothing to enjoy an already sizable place in the sun. The Channel had been crossed by Bleriot, the Medi-

Smithsonian's National Air and Space Museum

The Wright Brothers had been honored by the Smithsonian's presentation of the Langley Medal in 1910 by this group. Left to right are: Dr. Charles D. Walcott, secretary of the Smithsonian; Wilbur Wright; Dr. Alexander Graham Bell; and Orville Wright, entering a taxi which was capable of providing room for a high hat.

terranean by Garros, the American continent by Cal Rodgers. The 1913 Gordon Bennett race had raised the speed record to 105 miles per hour. Lt. B. Q. Jones in a Martin *TT* raised the American nonstop record to 8 hours 53 minutes at San Diego. Captain H. LeR. Muller raised the American altitude record in a Curtiss to 16,800 feet. Victor Carlstrom made an impressive flight from Toronto to New York nonstop, a distance of 400 miles, in six hours in a new Curtiss *R2* biplane. The name of Wright appeared on no new records. Rising war clouds were pushing European governments into accelerating their military flying activities. But except for the Mexican border troubles, the United States was busy mainly with expanding training. The industry was in an expectant mood but due to low profit on government orders, it was hard pressed for cash. Some money was still dribbling in from the exhibition business. The Wright patent bogeyman was not yet put away.

Planes were selling for $4 to $8 a pound, empty. Mechanics were getting $24 a week.

5 Uncertain Days Ahead

THE AVIATION WORLD in America now faced uncertain days under war threat conditions. The country knew that sooner or later we would be drawn into the conflict despite the vote-seeking assurances of political powers in Washington. President Woodrow Wilson would "keep us out of war," but industrial America was not averse to turning its ploughshares into guns if an honest business penny could be earned. When these American-made munitions would be on their way to Europe to destroy Germans, anyone with sense could figure that the Germans would do their best to prevent them from getting there. The most effective way to stop this traffic was by using submarines to sink Allied freighters that were carrying these loads of raw materials, guns, planes, fuel and other war-making necessities desperately needed by the British and the French. With bated breath citizens of the forty-eight states kept their fingers crossed while the orders started pouring in.

For the aircraft industry the needs of our own country were the object of much wishful thinking, some sensible planning, and quite a lot of scandalmongering. There was still that nuisance threat over the aircraft manufacturers' way to a profitable life—the Wright patent. So far the monopoly-minded Wright Company seemed to have indicated that they expected at least 20 percent of any profits that air munitions or any other aircraft operations would earn. This was too heavy a price. Many ethical and honest Americans were beginning to condemn the Wright Company, editorially and otherwise, for claiming too much at a very touchy time for the country's good. In late 1914 Curtiss had been sued again by Wright, and this case was again being prolonged by every possible legal subterfuge. Simultaneously, all kinds of influences outside of the court proceedings were being exercised to gain public sympathy for the harassed Curtiss Company as well as for others in aviation who were threatened. The Wright Company was becoming unpopular.

At Hammondsport, Curtiss continued to try out every variation of ailerons: trailing edge between the wings, operated singly, hinged in various ways with no rudder connection, and other, hopefully patent-free, means of lateral control. There remained in Curtiss' mind that tantalizing "Clause 1" of the Wright patent, which had not yet been adjudicated in the January 1914 decision. This clause specified in an airplane surface means "whereby said lateral marginal portions may be moved . . . so as to present to the atmosphere, different angles of incidence." It was supposed to cover all manner of ailerons, but it was not yet law. Optimistically, it could still be found unsustainable and invalid. Hopes grew on this and the Curtiss forces received sanguine support from many quarters. First, Henry Ford became friendly with Curtiss and arranged for him to have the expert legal aid of Judge Benton Crisp, who had recently broken the basic Selden automobile patent and saved Ford and so many others in this field from that burden.

There was a flood of articles and lectures hostile to the Wrights. Many were written by Dr. A. F. Zahm, the aeronautical expert who had testified for Curtiss in earlier suits and who had become the head of the revived Langley Laboratory at the Smithsonian. Zahm wrote repeatedly that the airplane was "a

Smithsonian's National Air and Space Museum

The Langley *Aerodrome* ready for launching.

public invention, a public possession, participated in by many early inventors. Cayley, Henson, Ader, Maxim, Lillienthal, Langley . . . no one should be permitted to dominate the aeroplane industry." And so on.

It was only a short step, therefore, for Glenn Curtiss to propose to Dr. Charles D. Walcott, Secretary and head of the great and respected Smithsonian Institution, taking the old original Langley *Aerodrome* out of storage, near the museum, and sending it to Hammondsport. Then "by merely mounting it on floats" (as Curtiss had done with his own planes) they could eliminate the launching catapult that many believed had caused Langley's failure. The world would then learn, after all, that the Langley plane could have flown; that it antedated the Wrights and that all this talk about the Wrights' being the only "pioneers" was ridiculous.

And so, before the last gasp of the patent threat, something very shameful took place in American science. Walcott used his authority at the Smithsonian's National Museum to direct, without approval of the board of regents of the museum, that the Langley plane be taken out of storage, dusted off and sent to Hammondsport, so that Curtiss could mount it on floats and fly it. For this job Walcott was even paying Curtiss $2,000. There is no doubt that Walcott and his aide Zahm imagined that they were to become unsung secret heroes who would have rescued aviation from the "steal" they pictured the Wright Company as trying to get away with, and at the same time immortalize the memory of Walcott's predecessor, Secretary Langley. They conveniently forgot what scientific ethics they were violating. Zahm profited by all this; he was a paid "consultant" and "patent expert" for Curtiss. There is no evidence that Walcott was other than gullible, no doubt considerably influenced by Zahm and by zeal for his friend Langley's memory.

Curtiss and his mechanics got to work, with Dr. Zahm as the official "observer." After much struggling in complete secrecy at the Curtiss plant, it took them from April 14 to May 28, 1914, to bring the *Aerodrome* out in the open, mounted on floats for its first flight. Some "slight changes" of course had to be made to accommodate the floats. For example, it was just a mere coincidence that the bracing of the float structure also happened to brace the wings, so that they could not bend up at the rear when the center of pressure moved back to that rear position that Langley knew nothing about. Walcott inspected the changes in person. Perhaps he did not notice that the rudder control had been altered; that the engine had a few "slight changes" in the carburetor and the ignition, like making them both new and more modern. Thirty-five other changes in the original *Aerodrome* had been made, all listed at a later date by Orville Wright.

The Langley *Aerodrome*—now a 1914 model—was pushed into the water, carefully and gently. Few witnesses were allowed at first to be present. When the wind had calmed down enough, it was towed out into the lake. Photographers followed closely. The pilot taxied about 1,000 feet and then just managed to hop off the water for a five-second jump before flopping back. But the photographer won the laurels of the day. He snapped a picture of what, sure enough, looked like Langley's famous plane free of the earth, soaring in the air!

(A similar tactic of having an alert quick-on-the-trigger photographer was used to excite the public by Howard Hughes

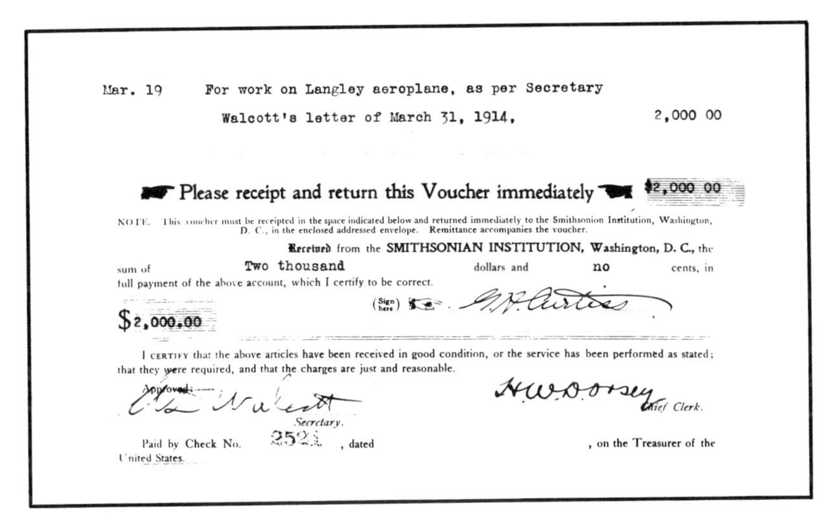

Mar. 19 For work on Langley aeroplane, as per Secretary Walcott's letter of March 31, 1914, 2,000 00

Please receipt and return this Voucher immediately $2,000 00

NOTE. This voucher must be receipted in the space indicated below and returned immediately to the Smithsonian Institution, Washington, D. C., in the enclosed addressed envelope. Remittance accompanies the voucher.

Received from the SMITHSONIAN INSTITUTION, Washington, D. C., the sum of Two thousand dollars and no cents, in full payment of the above account, which I certify to be correct.

(Sign here) G. H. Curtiss

$2,000.00

I CERTIFY that the above articles have been received in good condition, or the service has been performed as stated; that they were required, and that the charges are just and reasonable.

Approved: C. D. Walcott, Secretary.

H. W. Dorsey, Chief Clerk.

Paid by Check No. 252[illegible], dated , on the Treasurer of the United States.

Smithsonian's National Air and Space Museum

The voucher for the Curtiss-Walcott deal.

This photograph of the Langley was published by the Smithsonian, with the legend shown.

many, many years later. This was in 1947 when we were shown a photo of that great giant flying boat soaring through the air, snapped on its one and only short hop off the waters of San Pedro Bay, never to fly again . . . left to gather dust in its hangar ever since.)

So with widely disseminated pictures to prove it, the respected and dignified Smithsonian Institution under the direction of its Secretary stated in its Annual Report for 1914:

> The original Langley Aerodrome, without modification has flown at last. It has demonstrated that with its original structure and power, it is capable of flying with a pilot and several hundred pounds of useful load. It is the first aeroplane in the history of the world of which this can truthfully be said.

Without modifications? This "Hammondsport Hoax," however, did its job quite well. People, including some very important ones, were convinced that the Wrights had gotten away with a prestige they did not deserve. And Benton Crisp, who had gloated over the influence this would have on the continuing patent litigation, urged that the Langley flight tests be extended into 1915 for the purpose of further befuddling the courts. So a new, modern motor was installed and the weak, wrongly designed wings reinforced (though not strengthened enough). The controls were improved, the pontoons redesigned for better takeoff, and that important photographer no doubt furnished with new cameras and more assistants. The Wright patent suit, now claiming that Curtiss' single-acting aileron (only one side pulled down, with no cross-connection to lift the other side) was also an infringement, was about to go to court, and Crisp was doing everything possible to delay while his propaganda was undermining the primacy of the Wrights.

About the time when the 1915 model of the much changed *Aerodrome* was ready for its trials, a small, fortyish, unprepossessing man with a graying moustache and wearing glasses,

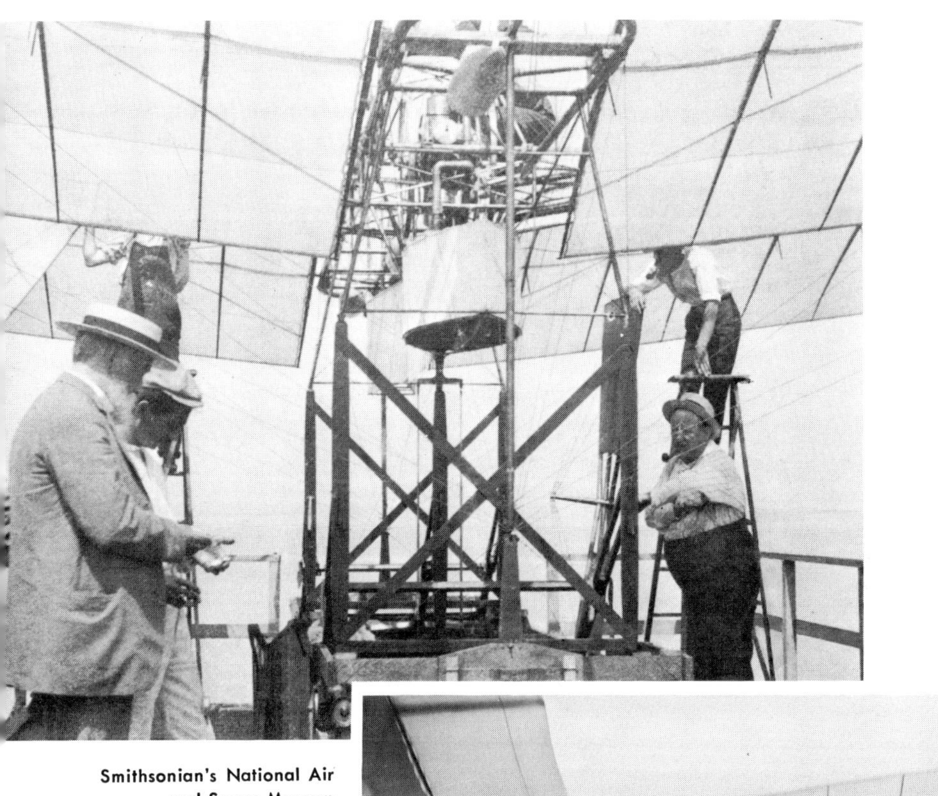

Smithsonian's National Air and Space Museum

The *Aerodrome* assembled on catapult. Dr. Langley (straw hat) and C. M. Manly at the left.

The plunge into the Potomac caused by the wings folding from sudden air forces.

registered at the hotel in Bath, New York, near Hammondsport, as Mr. W. L. Oren. He was seen daily hovering unobtrusively near the Langley plane and around the shore with his field glasses, as were many other spectators and hangers-on. He had a camera which he did not use until the tests of the much altered Langley were started. Then he used it openly enough to attract the attention of some Curtiss officials. As he was snapping his pictures, the Langley had just struggled off the water in full flight when suddenly the wings collapsed. There was great dismay. "You will have to give us that film," a Curtiss man told Mr. Oren, threateningly. "We cannot allow pictures because of legal complications." Quite obviously, the air pressure on the wings again had been too much for this further-altered version of the Langley machine. The wing collapse and the wreck that followed would have made dandy pictures. So this little man had to give up his film, which he did with understandable reluctance and regret, because he had so wanted to send all of this with his copious notes to his younger brother, Orville Wright. The "spy" was Lorin Wright and the collection of his letters on this episode is in itself a thriller.

As 1916 began, this court action was never to be completed. The wreckage of the Langley *Aerodrome* was returned to the Smithsonian, where, under the direction of Luther Reed, who had been one of Langley's mechanics, it was restored to its 1903 configuration and for the first time placed on exhibition. The label read, "first heavier-than-aircraft in the history of the world capable of sustained free flight under its own power carrying a man." This further angered Orville.

The famous Smithsonian-Wright controversy thus had its start and lasted with varying degrees of name-calling for the ensuing twenty years, involving charges by Orville Wright and his adherents that the Smithsonian had committed a fraud. For this reason, Wright sent his *Kitty Hawk Flyer*, the most important mechanical relic in man's history, on loan to the Science Museum at South Kensington in London. He refused to bring it back and send it where it belonged, the National Museum of its home country, until the Smithsonian in its Annual Report would admit to the changes and untruths, apologize for the outrageous statements of Walcott and Zahm, and change the Langley label to read "The Langley *Aerodrome* Restored" and the Wright plane label to read, "The World's First Successful Airplane." By 1947, a year before Orville's death, this was done, under the direction of Dr. C. G. Abbot, a more enlightened and fair Secretary. Now the *Kitty Hawk* proudly hangs where it belongs, and is viewed with awe by over 2,000,000 people a year.

Curtiss and Crisp had other reasons for delaying action on the patent situation. In 1915, the change in the Wright Company after Orville had sold out held promise of some kind of a reasonable deal being worked out. A fine representative businessman, Henry Lockhart, had been named the new president of the Wright Company; Orville, far away in Dayton, was merely a consultant, and no longer very influential in patent matters. The new Wright group were distinctly not Wall Street speculators or promoters. Although bankers Charles Sabin, Albert Wiggin and Harvey Gibson were directors, the new owners were more or less dedicated to manufacturing. They considered the patent matter a side issue. This was evidenced by their moves in adding to the basic Wright Company new mergers with several other outfits. First there was the purchase and absorption of the Simplex Automobile Company. This was followed in September 1916 by the merger with the Glenn Martin Company, and then later with the General Aeronautic Company of America. All were put in one package called the Wright-Martin Aircraft Company, capitalized at $10,000,000.

Henry M. Crane, a great automotive engineer, was sent to Europe to conduct a firsthand survey on the requirements of the war munitions business. Crane returned to his duties as vice-president and chief engineer of Wright-Martin with a contract for the highly successful French Hispano-Suiza eight-cylinder, 150-horsepower airplane motor. This was just going into production for fighter planes and would almost certainly be widely used. It was a complex design with a very difficult casting requirement, but Crane and his Crane-Simplex automobile group, with their reputation for top workmanship, were fully equal to the task. Although Curtiss had already received large orders for the *JN* training plane from England, the signing of the Hispano-Suiza manufacturing license by Wright-Martin, accompanied with an order from France for 450 motors, was the first really big air-munitions contract awarded to the United States by France. It was soon followed in 1916 by many others, among them orders for French rotary engines, Gnome and Le Rhone, given to the General Vehicle Company and the Union Switch and Signal Company.

"Preparedness" now became the call in many phases of American life. Reserve units for aviation began to grow at universities and in National Guard quarters. At the beginning most of these were financed by private contributions. Not only was the national government tardy in pushing defense activities, but Wilson's Administration was still trying to convince Europe and America that we were neutral. Among the new air units that were outstanding in this helpful wave to increase our strength should we finally be involved in war were the Yale Unit for Naval Aviation headed by Trubee Davison; and an initial Army Reserve Aero Squadron of the Militia based at New York and fathered by lawyers Reynal Bolling and Phillip Carroll. The Yale Unit purchased Curtiss *F* boats, and the Aero Squadron started off with *Sturtevant* tractors, and then obtained Curtiss *JN's*.

Progress in the U. S. air services was painfully slow, limited as it was by still-scanty appropriations and tepid public interest. Most of the activity centered around expanding schools, and the only military action had to do with the series of Mexican incidents. First there were raids near the border, then the 1914 Navy occupation of Vera Cruz to discipline Victoriano Huerta, and finally, Pershing's 1916 expedition to try to capture the rebel Pancho Villa. In this operation the First Aero Squadron proved to be a dismal failure—so futile that a Congressional investigation (the first one on aviation) was staged to appease the shocked public. The old training planes had failed miserably because of the climate and the high altitude needed for the flying operations. For this duty the U. S. Signal Corps Aviation Section was utterly lacking in proper equipment. The flying officers themselves were the chief instigators of this investigation. They claimed that the ineptness of their superiors was due to the fact that they were not flyers and were woefully incompetent to run an air service, a theme destined to be repeated many times in the hectic future.

The progress of Curtiss at this period was rapid and significant. As already mentioned, the factory at Hammondsport had become quite inadequate and the two then-separate outfits, Curtiss Aeroplane Company and Curtiss Motor Company, were merged in early 1916 into a single larger unit called the Curtiss Aeroplane and Motor Company. The headquarters and main factory were moved to Buffalo, New York. At this time, a new and very different influence entered the manufacturing life of Glenn Curtiss. He went into partnership with one of the largest and most prominent automobile promoters and producers, John N. Willys, of Willys-Overland fame, who bought a large stock interest in the Curtiss Company. Curtiss also brought into the merger the Burgess and Curtis Company (designer Starling Burgess of yacht fame and Greeley Curtis) and several smaller companies.

Three other important new companies came on the scene during this period. The B. F. Sturtevant Company of Boston made all types of blowers and air pumps. Ex-Governor Foss of Massachusetts saw the coming war manufacturing opportunity and had his engineers design and develop an 8-cylinder, 150-horsepower aircraft motor. It tested out quite well on power for weight ratio, and high hopes were held for it. Foss created the Sturtevant Aeroplane Company to build planes for this engine. Burgess was already building a pusher scouting type for Canada, using this motor on one of the earliest war orders. Other nations, notably Russia, and Argentina, were interested in the Sturtevant motor, and so were the U.S. Army and Navy.

Since at this date we were already learning how vitally important it was for a new airplane to have an adequately tested motor, designers like myself were much intrigued by something other and with more power than the widely used Curtiss OX-5. Therefore when the Sturtevant Company proposed that I leave the Army and come with them as engineer, I accepted, having high hopes for several new fighter plane designs that I had been studying. These were based on many war requirements and features that had been reported by World War I participants and observers. What I did not learn until long and weary months later was that the stand on which the Sturtevant motor showed up so well had failed to disclose a deficiency that dogged us through the life of all our planes using this engine. The trouble, almost a tragic one, was in the water-pumping system for cooling the engine. The pump was entirely inadequate and so installed that it pumped "steam pockets" which caused all the different radiators that were used to heat up in flight. This failure never showed up on the test stand. The result was a series of futile designs, none of which attained any notable success . . . an opportunity lost at a very crucial time. The war was breathing hard on our necks and influencing our thoughts. Our *Battleplane*, a fine, big two-seater with two gun turrets, was one project. Another was a small *Speed Scout* that Lieutenant Milling at San Diego had helped design. The success of both planes would have meant much. Their pioneer spot-welded steel construction stirred a lot of interest. But we could not get enough flying out of them because of the frustrating motor. When the suggestion was made to use some other motor, the Foss family turned it down.

Financed by Mitsui, Japanese bankers, Standard Aircraft started at Elizabeth, New Jersey, with expert Charles Day as engineer. Another promising, fast-growing company was the Thomas-Morse Aeroplane Company of Ithaca, New York. This was a combination of the Thomas brothers, who had been doing exhibition flying and plane construction, joined up with the rich Morse Chain Company. This company rapidly showed high competence, and they were at work on a single-seater fighter that was ahead of its time. There were several other capable outfits growing very fast, like the L.W.F. Company on Long Island, where expert Charles Willard worked; the Witteman-Lewis Company in Newark, New Jersey; Chance Vought had started his small plant in Long Island City; the Loening Aeronautical Engineering Company, which was just coming to life in New York; and Inglis Uppercu, had already put into active life his Aeromarine Company, which was to do fine work for the Navy, and to survive after the war as a vigorous airline pioneer.

Curtiss, too, was at work on many new projects, such as the *Model R's* with their 200-horsepower motors, a considerable advance over the OX-5 and the *Jennie*. His engineer, Charles Kirkham, was on the threshold of producing some fine new engines. In addition, Curtiss was moving speedily in flying-boat development, one or two-engined, increasingly seaworthy designs, and on their way to wide acceptance ahead of any other nation.

As the difficult and unrewarding year of 1917 opened up the American air industry had much more in resources and trained personnel than appeared on the surface. Little did the public know of this and the industry did not anticipate the manner in which it was about to be downgraded.

The airplane personnel were mostly young, and they had not yet organized any kind of Washington-oriented lobby or trade association, as had the automobile companies. No articulate spokesmen, no press coverage. The U.S. had almost as many trained engineers as there were in Europe. From M.I.T., Donald Douglas and Thomas Huff had been graduated under the tutelage of Jerome Hunsaker (who had been trained by Eiffel). From Cornell came Roy Grumman, from Columbia myself, and from several other engineering schools we had Larry Bell, Chance Vought, Charles Willard and Charles Day.

The Europeans in the same age bracket were Sidney Camm (England), Handley Page, Frank Barnwell and Roy Fedden (England), Geoffrey de Havilland and Anthony Fokker (Holland), Edward Nieuport and Jacques Morane (France), and Igor Sikorsky (Russia). U.S. aircraft engineers were as well trained and familiar with aircraft manufacturing as their European equivalents. The only real difference was that the experience of our personnel had been built up in civilian and exhibition flying, and not actually in war-oriented planes. This difference could be and was exaggerated. Mounting a gun on a well-built, fine-flying plane was not too difficult, and it would give a better end product than that achieved by applying military equipment to a "clunker" plane, built by European engineers who were in a hurry to get any plane to the front. The various *Voisins, Caudrons, Moranes, F.E.* pushers, *Salmsons, Albatrosses, Pfalzes,* and other efforts abroad were planes of the latter class.

Then, too, America had its outstanding first-generation airplane engine pioneers—Wright, Curtiss, Henry Crane, and Charles Lawrance—who were quite as experienced and talented in producing engines as the Levavaseurs, Anzanis, Daimlers and Birkigts of Europe. They could give the Europeans tough competition as inspiring leaders of the young engineering and manufacturing experts that the United States already had in the back room.

As to the manufacturing facilities: except for Curtiss, Martin and Standard Aircraft and for motors, Crane's Simplex plant at New Brunswick, Curtiss at Buffalo and Hall-Scott in California, we were behind Europe chiefly on floor space in use (merely because it was in Europe that the governments had spent money for war production). As for lack of floor space, this much-used argument against the U. S. background for warplane production proved to be nonsense. It took practically no time for concrete and steel to be whisked magically onto a flying field site. The craft to be built within such walls was the payoff. Were there imaginative and skilled engineers in the drafting room?

Undeniably, at the end of 1916 there was no plane in the U.S. armed forces with a gun on it ready to fire. But our designers had their drawings ready for a military order, if they could get one. "Remember . . . we are supposed to be neutral," was the excuse. There were aircraft radio installations ready, and Sherman Fairchild, then only twenty years old, was already developing equipment for aerial photography, in which he was shortly to lead the world.

The real trouble with American aviation at the beginning of 1917 was stagnation, due first of all to scant impetus from Government appropriations. From 1908 to 1913, the total of all U. S. Congressional appropriations for aircraft had totaled $435,000—less than $100,000 a year. During the same period, Germany, for example, had voted and used $28,000,000. Our previously greater exhibition, or private, market had dried up because of the war jitters. A prevailing uncertainty hung like a veil over the ambitions of Martin, Chance Vought, Thomas, Crane, Lawrance, and Loening personnel, so eager to prove the war value and potential of aviation. America, at the dawn of 1917, had plenty of strength, promise, and sound ability and experience in its existing aircraft industry, to embark on a highly successful and effective contribution to warplane production. The world was to be told otherwise. And the most shameful misuse of American talent was about to show its deplorable results.

Archives Bureau

The Aircraft Production Board of 1917. Right to left: Howard E. Coffin, chairman; Maj. Gen. George O. Squier, Army; Adm. D. W. Taylor, Navy; Edward A. Deeds, Dayton, Ohio; Sydney D. Waldon, Detroit, Michigan; Robert Montgomery, Phiadelphia banker; and A. G. Cable, secretary. None of these had ever had experience in aircraft production. All the civilians were identified with the automobile business.

6 Copying Didn't Work

WHEN my friend, the prominent Dayton, Ohio, attorney John Hayward, invited me to join him in a late Sunday evening snack at the residence of the Delco "starter" inventor, Charles F. Kettering, I thought it would be a social occasion. Also there was Edward A. Deeds, an officer of the National Cash Register Company (the "Cash" to all Daytonians), who with Kettering had organized the Delco Company. Others who dropped in were Harold E. Talbott, a Dayton banker and builder, and his son Harold, Jr. The latter I knew from my Wright Company days.

Naïvely, I guessed that the showing of "Ket" Kettering's new and impressive pipe organ was the reason for the assemblage. It was not long before I learned other interesting matters were to be discussed.

"Have you seen Mr. Wright?" asked Deeds. . . . No, I had not as yet.

"Are you getting along O.K. at the Sturtevant Company?" asked Ket. The answer was a firm affirmative. It was early 1916 and the work was just getting underway.

"Well," said Deeds, "you know we are all doing a lot of

thinking about the flying business around here. Orville has sold his company and retired to do research. We've been thinking of forming an outfit here to keep Dayton as the world center of aviation. Howard Rinehart, the test pilot and instructor—you know him—is being set up by us in a flying school. Orville is building his new laboratory now and may join up with us in keeping Dayton on the airplane map." I quickly gathered the "us" meant Deeds, Kettering and Talbott.

Kettering, in his high-pitched, Ohio-accented voice, joined in above the organ strains, "You know, if the U.S. does get into this war, we want to help do it right. We are building a new factory for Domestic Lighting Company down here in Moraine, near this house. In a jiffy we could turn this into a plane plant if it was needed." He changed the organ tone and proceeded. "Our Dayton Metal Products Company boys are in this war game right now, making fuses for Russia and England, and we're set up to make anything in that company, aren't we?" Looking at Deeds, there was a characteristic distinct wink from Ket. My respect for these men made me feel sure a worthwhile contribution for war could be made . . . if they only knew aviation.

But they didn't. Years later, John Hayward and I often talked about that evening. He had been one of the lawyers for this group, knew the real story on what developed as well as anyone, and was able to explain much about the failure of Deeds' program.

The Dayton group of Deeds (as the leader), Kettering, Harold Talbott, Sr., and Harold Jr., formed the Dayton-Wright Airplane Company, with Orville Wright as a nonworking director. They were all convinced that they could make a great contribution to our warmaking strength and efficiency by having a closely knit consortium of their own take over the Government's aviation planning and direction while everyone else was asleep. The profits would be big and justified. They had a good labor market for airplane construction in Dayton. Deeds had told many people, including John Hayward, Rinehart, and

Army Air persons in Washington, how favorably they were situated. Auto body workers from the recently closed Maxwell plant were available. Skilled metal-fitting men from the "Cash" and from many home industries were unemployed. Building those wood-and-wire frame, fabric-covered planes seemed to Deeds to be "a cinch for these fellers." Hayward had once asked Deeds, "How about the existing plane builders?" And he got the answer, "They're just a lot of kids playing with toys . . . know nothing about production, except for Curtiss."

Others, including my associate Henry M. Crane (who later became a director of the Loening Company), recalled how confident Deeds was about the easy time they would have of breaking into aviation in a big way. Only two things were needed, according to Deeds: a motor hookup with Detroit, and drawings from the English and French missions, detailing what was wanted.

The connection with Detroit was soon effected. Sidney Waldon, vice-president of Packard, and Jesse C. Vincent, Packard engineer, were promptly brought into their plans. Vincent had already designed and tested a 12-cylinder motor along the lines of the Daimler and Mercedes engines in Germany, samples of which he had already obtained. Vincent had been using the Delco ignition system which Kettering had developed. This was being built in the Dayton Engineering Laboratories Company plant (Delco). A combination of resources and interests such as this was a "natural." Vincent insisted that they must install only American engines in any foreign copies of planes. "It would be so easy to do by approximating the same horsepower." Deeds agreed enthusiastically. "We'll call it the 'Liberty motor.'"

This plan had the powerful appeal of helping to win a war, accompanied by huge profits. Only one other ingredient was needed—a confidential and effective approach to Washington. This job was given to Howard E. Coffin, the sparkplug of the growing Society of Automotive Engineers, who was also vice-president of the large Hudson Motor Car Company. Coffin proceeded to organize the needed infiltration into the workings of the War Department, the Army Signal Corps and its Aviation Section.

Other regions and other industries of the country instead of Dayton could at this time have made similar moves to bring the bulk and center of future airplane activity to their locales. But the Dayton group moved too skillfully and swiftly in secret to be overtaken.

It is equally true that other industrial complexes could have been as qualified or as closely related to aircraft work as the Dayton consortium. In the case of the skilled quantity-production furniture manufacturers or the highly versatile builders of small boats like Elco, there is plenty of evidence that they could have done a much better job. But they were unwilling, not ready, or just asleep. The logical growth of the existing aeronautical people to meet war demands was firmly scotched except in the case of Curtiss. This is how it was done.

The infiltration took place very adroitly in early 1916, with war clouds clearly forming. Howard Coffin went down to Washington, and in his position as active head of the growing Society of Automotive Engineers (S.A.E.) put all his propaganda machinery to work with assistance from Michigan and Ohio Senators. He was able to convince the Council of National Defense, and particularly his personal friend, Brig. Gen. George O. Squier of the Aviation Section, Signal Corps, U. S. Army, that his freely offered services at $1 a year should be accepted at once. It was obvious to all of them that a man of Coffin's ability and experience would mean much to them in clearing up technical headaches beyond their capacities. And indeed it did. Coffin was a politician, to be sure, but he also was highly competent and articulate. It was not long before his influence and effectiveness came close to that of Bernard Baruch and Colonel Edward House in the inner councils of President Wilson on defense matters, mostly aeronautical. His indefatigable zeal went further, up into the cloak rooms and halls of Congress, where he helped immeasurably in gaining support for a series of ever-increasing aircraft appropriations. This naturally endeared him ever more to the heads of the air arms of the two services.

Meanwhile, Henry Souther, automotive associate and friend of Coffin, a publicist, lecturer and very delightful and impressive personality, first offered his services as a consultant and then enlisted as a civilian reservist in the Signal Corps. Now, whether by Coffin's influence with Squier or not, this engaging man soon became Major Souther in the uniform of the U. S. Army Signal Corps attached to the office of the Chief Signal Officer, General Squier himself. So the Aviation Section had acquired the services of a no doubt helpful assistant while the Dayton coterie had a friend, if not an actual associate, in the back room. Souther became a ubiquitous person at all aircraft occasions, technical meetings, banquets, tests of new aircraft; in fact, he became part of the scenery of the air.

What a relief it must have been to Secretary of War Newton Baker and General Squier to know that the weighty problems of secret preparations for quantity production of aircraft and engines were being efficiently studied and worked out by the brilliant group of men from the esteemed automotive industry!

And how easy it was, therefore, for the heads of the Government's aircraft departments to accept the assessment of these promoters from Dayton about the then-existing small aircraft manufacturers and their young engineers.

"They seem to be asleep, these air people, or unaware of what an emergency we are already in." This was only too true, and excusable only on the ground that Martin, Vought, Day, Douglas, Loening, Thomas and others were busy studying the war situation, working on new designs, new methods of construction, welded steel framing, veneer covering for fuselages, better streamlining, etc., to give better service than that of the exhibition machines they had been building for years. They had not thought much of their business future or how it was about to be affected by the happenings in Washington. There were other whispered comments.

"The small aircraft manufacturers haven't enough floor space

Smithsonian's National Air and Space Museum

This new factory was still unfinished when the Dayton-Wright Company received its first war order.

to make even a dent on the war's requirements." This was not true of Curtiss nor of such others as Martin and Standard, who were just starting to acquire larger floor space, newly built, and with bigger financing. In fact, when the Dayton group started selling their possible ability to build planes in great quantity, the Dayton-Wright plant, originally designed for Kettering's Domestic Engineering Company (small power plants for farms), was not yet completed. The Government was occasionally misled on this "availability of huge existing automotive plants." Many of the companies that took over the aircraft program actually had to build or have the Government build totally new plants near flying fields, with higher ceilings and bigger doors. All of these, incidentally, came in handy for auto purposes when the war ended.

Another comment. "The existing plane designers have no ability to build war machines, since no American plane has been delivered with guns mounted. We will have to get European designers for this kind of work." This was a telling criticism, and a misleading one. It was much easier than at first supposed to mount guns and other items if it were done by competent, versatile aircraft people. But when the auto people (unfamiliar with exacting aircraft "tricks") started on their own to mount this equipment on foreign copies, they made a sorry mess.

Our designers had a lot of proficiency in aerodynamics, acquired in exhibition flying, where demands of diving and stunt-

Smithsonian's National Air and Space Museum

Dayton-Wright production under way with difficulties on the 4,000 *DH-4* plane order that never materialized.

ing stresses had to be met that were less understood in Europe. Fighting planes at the front were pulling their wings off time and again in sharp maneuvers because their designers had not been exposed to the requirements of this kind of flying. When the British *DH-4* was brought here, American designers took one look (after they were asked to) and laughed at the front bracing to the wings for diving stresses. To them it was obviously weak and inadequate, as was the faulty bracing of the stabilizer. But it was not obvious at all to the air production people. Sure enough, as soon as the diving tests of the *DH-4* were started, the plane fell apart, and two of our best pilots were killed. Other criticisms of our struggling aircraft makers were voiced repeatedly by the auto men. Our aviation people, not knowing what was being said so convincingly against their ability, lost out. This planned propaganda was effective, and since it was not denied, Washington had little confidence in the existing American aircraft background. Orville Wright could have stopped this false trend, but he did nothing. Apparently, he did not appreciate how this was weakening U. S. potential. Perhaps his tie with the Deeds group made him feel he should agree with their appraisals. The case against using native designers and builders was further clinched by the convincing way visiting foreign missions (asked for and cordially hailed by General Squier) joined the chorus of scorn for American designing ability.

The unanimous refrain was that lacking any qualifications of our own to build warplanes, all the United States could do to help in the war was for the U. S. to devote its entire effort to building copies of foreign designs. This was the policy adopted and made effective a few days after we declared war on April 6th, 1917. French Premier Georges Clemenceau asked for 5,000 pilots and 4,000 planes by January 1918; a production schedule of 2,000 planes and 4,000 engines a month, thereafter.

It took less than a year for the dream plan of Coffin and Deeds on meeting this schedule to blow up in their faces. One after another the copies were a fiasco. The only part of this incompetently planned program that succeeded was the one element that was not a copy—the Liberty motor!

Right after war was declared, I felt that more should be asked of me than fussing with the unrewarding Sturtevant situation, so I took a vacation and went to Washington. I called on the Army and found that there was little they definitely wanted me to do (yet I had been the Army's first aircraft engineer). I called on the Navy and they at once wanted me to go to England as technical advisor to the Naval attaché. Before leaving, I saw Dr. Walcott and others of the National Advisory Committee for Aeronautics. They, too, urged me to go to London and asked me to give them a review of what I saw immediately on my return.

Part of the Navy duty was to look over a fleet of *Short* seaplanes that the British were trying to sell to the United States. After careful examination, study of the Sunbeam motor, conferences far into the night at the Aero Club with pilots who had flown them, and after flying one myself, I learned that they were duds. They would hardly get off the water with any kind of load, leaked badly, had a serious tail flutter, and in performance didn't compare with a Curtiss *HS* boat. Therefore, I recommended that the United States refuse the proffered deal. This the Navy did.

I also had complete access to many warplane construction operations, flew frequently with Capt. Frank Barnwell in his

Bristol *Fighter* and with Captain Hucks in the then-new *DH-4* de Havilland with Rolls-Royce 350-horsepower motor. It was a fine flying machine, but I thought it flimsily built for its admittedly high performance. I saw many details in its structure that we in the American industry would not countenance, and thought the visibility and gun mount were poor.

On my return, a meeting at the National Advisory Committee for Aeronautics was held at once and I reported all I had found. Included was a recommendation to build various war types of our own design. I explained fully that by the time we had gotten drawings and samples of planes from foreign sources, we could have made our own versions without all the metric system translation headaches and delays entailed in trying to make copies.

I was sure that our own engineers, like Glenn Martin, could meet the war performances needed in speed, climb, range, etc. The relatively simple guns and bomb gear could be mounted without great trouble. After all, the French were not building any British machines for the British, nor were the latter building any foreign ones. It was only engines and guns, not airframes. We could go along in the same way because we already had in America the production of the Hispano and Gnome motors and could go to higher powers and other makes.

I could not help but note that my presentation was being received with little interest and few questions. In the audience were several Aviation Section officers whom I did not know. I was disappointed that my old Dayton friend, Edward Deeds, was not there. Several of my Navy friends, however, showed great interest.

In the next few days I learned what had happened while I was away. Both Glenn Martin and Chance Vought were in Washington at that time, and we conferred frequently on the incredible situation.

The Dayton team had indeed succeeded in their well thought out and effectively executed plan. In May 1917, the Council of National Defense established the Aircraft Production Board, with Howard E. Coffin as chairman and Edward Deeds and Sidney Waldon as members. This board formulated the airplane programs, and contracts were placed on its recommendations. Deeds was obviously the boss.

The best description of how they were getting to work to build planes in a hurry is Glenn Martin's experience as related in Henry Still's biography, *To Ride the Wind.* Martin called on the Signal Corps Aviation Section office. After much waiting he was ushered in to see a rather weary-looking lieutenant.

> "I wish to build military planes for the U.S. Army," said Glenn directly.
>
> "How many planes can you turn out, say, in a day?" the lieutenant demanded.
>
> "Three," Glenn shot back; he was stretching the truth a little, but he was anxious to show what his new factory might do.
>
> The other man sighed, began shaking his head negatively. . . . "I'm afraid," he said, "that won't do, Mr. Martin. Too slow. We must have thousands of planes as quickly as possible—overnight, if we can."
>
> A challenging note of hostility crept into Glenn's voice as he asked, "Just how do you expect to achieve that miracle?"
>
> "Automobiles," the lieutenant replied cryptically. . . . "The auto manufacturers have told us they can turn out 100,000 planes in the next two years. The aircraft manufacturers cannot even approach that; you have been geared to turning planes out practically by hand . . . frankly, we can't even consider any bids under twenty planes a day."
>
> Controlling the anger he felt rising, Glenn asked, "Have you seen any planes the auto people have produced?"
>
> "No, of course not," the lieutenant said. "We haven't got the blueprints yet. We've decided upon using the British de Havilland—the DH-4—as the best suited for our mass production approach."

This was a second blow: not only were the aircraft manufacturers being sidestepped, but the Army wasn't even interested in an American design! Glenn Martin rose and said bitterly, "Don't ask the soldiers in the front lines to wait for those planes —the war will be over before they ever reach France." Turning, he left the office, carrying in his briefcase—unopened—the drawings of the *MB1,* which was eventually to be the best bomber of any nation built for the war. It was delayed in production by this policy so that it never got to the front. The *MB1,* however, became our postwar leader.

Chance Vought had a similar experience. Within a day or so, I was treated to the same routine. When we got together to compare notes, it was Chance who said, "These guys don't know what a tragedy they are brewing. The copies will be too late to be any good at the front because they will be out of date, while we American designers can't seem to break in to get going."

The Navy was far more rational than the Army during this confusing and hectic Washington runaround. Both Vought and I got small contracts from the Navy that kept us barely in business while we all stood by, aghast at the debacle in the making.

Congress had voted $640,000,000 for Army aviation! Months went by during which the world heard a lot of fancy press yarns about how the great aircraft production program was breaking all records. Although troubles for the auto group started rather soon, the misleading publicity continued. Drawings received from Europe were wrong or incomplete. Changes were coming in from the front. Demands had to be met at once, some signed, peremptorily, "Pershing." The civilian organization had to be changed to a military one. Deeds and Waldon were put in uniform, commissioned colonels of the Army Signal Corps staff. A new unit was established, the Equipment Division, with Colonel Deeds as the chief and Colonel Waldon as his assistant. Jesse Vincent and E. J. Hall, who had been credited jointly with designing the Liberty motor, were also commissioned. So the whole auto clique except Coffin and Ketter-

Smithsonian's National Air and Space Museum

The Dayton-Wright *DH-4* as originally produced.

ing were in the service and could really give orders. This they did. Orders were given to Dayton-Wright, Fisher Body (Detroit), and Engel Aircraft (a new Cleveland outfit) for *DH-4* airplane frames; to Packard, Ford, Lincoln (the Leland Brothers, Detroit) and Marmon for Liberty motors. Curtiss received an order for 2,000 Bristol *Fighters*. After 27 that were built had killed four pilots, the order was canceled. The *S.E.5* fighter was also ordered built by Curtiss, but only a few got started. Also abortive were orders for the *Spad* fighter and for *Handley-Page* and *Caproni* bombers. Samples of the bombers were built. They were still being tested when the war ended.

In June 1917, General Squier had issued a statement, "We are sending myriads of airplanes over the German lines to teach Germany that we have come to win." On that date the Dayton-Wright factory was not yet quite finished, but the contract negotiations for Dayton-Wright's plane operations were underway. In his report later, investigator Charles Evans Hughes states, "The Dayton-Wright Airplane Company was launched about the time of our entry into the war, manifestly with the expectation of obtaining Goverment contracts." Expectation! Was it all cut and dried? On August 1, 1917, the first big war aircraft contract was awarded to this company for 400 *Standard J* training planes as a starter to fill the space until the British drawings arrived. Eventually, 4,000 *DH-4* military observation planes were ordered. This contract totaled over $30,000,000, and on a cost-plus—fixed-profit basis, the profit would have run to over $4,000,000.

Nothing wrong with this if the production had been successful. The first sample plane from England was delivered August 14, and with much overtime, what purported to be the first few U. S. Army *DH-4*'s made their first flights in November 1917. Shortly thereafter, tragic accidents dogged them, and factory personnel were bedeviled by hundreds of changes they had to make. So new were they to this kind of routine airplane development procedure that they were panic-stricken. Delays and more delays . . . excuses and more excuses. It took until May 1918 for the first 500 *DH-4*'s to be delivered, and then they were defective.

Finally came the outcry of disappointment in the press about reports from Europe that no American planes had showed up at the start of 1918, instead of the 4,000 promised. The vigorous undercurrent of scandal that followed was too much for the Administration. There was a sudden shift in personnel when the pathetic score of accomplishment was added up. After almost a year of Coffin-Deeds-Waldon management, of the 22,000 Liberty motors that had been ordered, with at least half promised for delivery by February 1918, only 600 had been turned over to the services (half to the Navy). The 400 Standard training planes ordered from Dayton-Wright had been delivered, but they had been condemned because of excessive vibration and fire danger from the rigid mounting of the 4-cylinder Hall-Scott motor. The *DH-4* production was far behind what had been promised so confidently. A year after we had declared war, not a single American plane had arrived at the scene of the war in Europe. No sign in Europe of the

U.S. Air Force

The Martin bomber *MB1*. Standing left to right are its creators: Larry Bell; Eric Springer; Glenn Martin; Donald Douglas.

eagerly awaited Dayton-Wright de Havilland until May 1918. And at that time this plane could not be used at the front because essential changes had to be made!

On February 18, 1918, less than a year after Colonel Deeds' takeover, the startling move was made to replace him as Chief of the Equipment Division, with William C. Potter, a New York banking and mining executive, very definitely not involved with an auto clique—just a keen, tough, sensible manager. One of his first actions was to call Glenn Martin to Washington to push him on his bomber contract. Then he arranged for Vought to build an advanced training plane; assigned the Loening Company to build a two-seater fighter; and Thomas-Morse to build a single-seater pursuit plane. This was the start of what should have been done at least eight months previously. By August 1918, only six months after these new designs had been given their go-ahead, they were

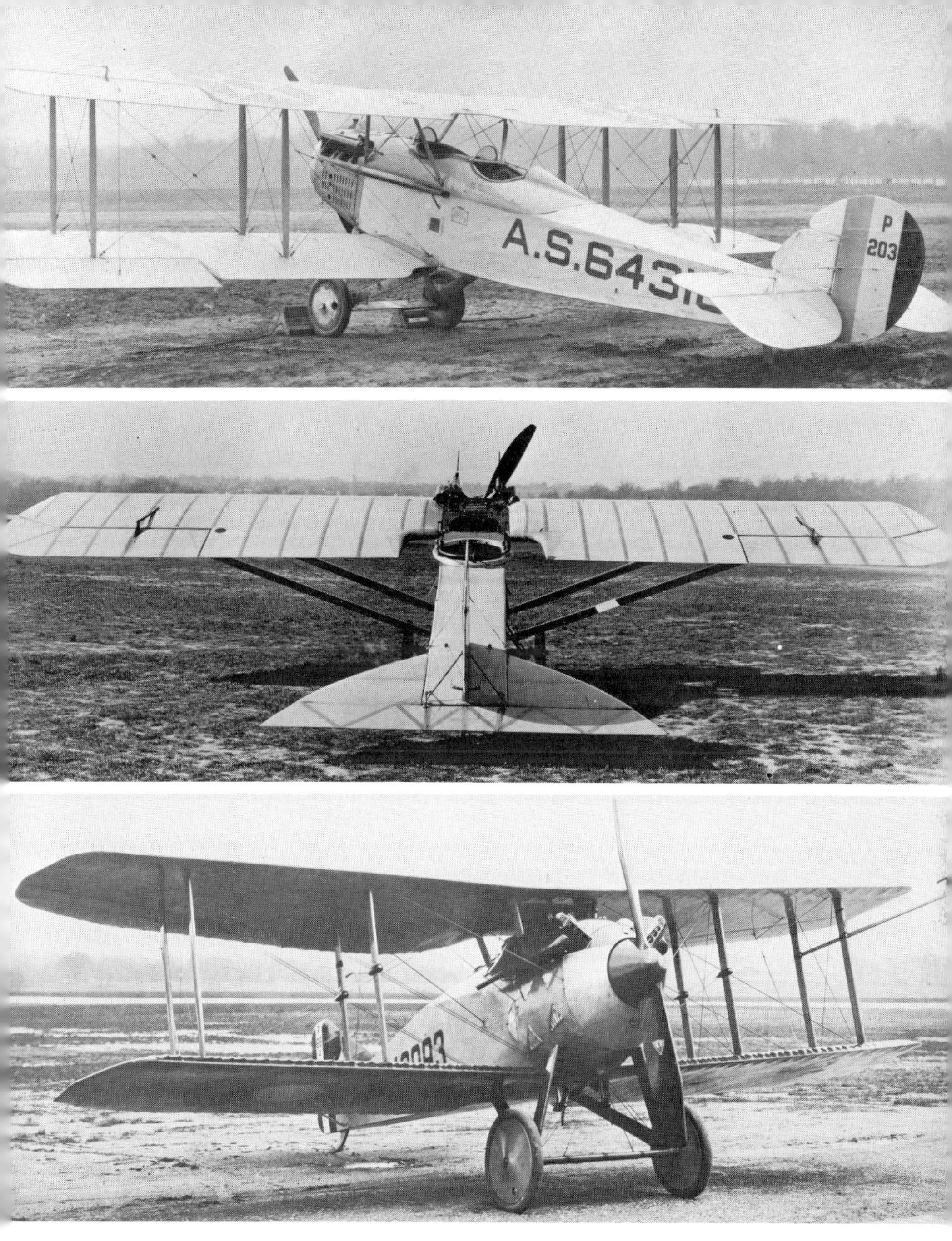

U.S. Air Force

The Vought two-seat trainer, Hispano motor.
The Loening *M8 0* monoplane two-seat fighter.
The Thomas-Morse *MB3* fighter, 300-horsepower Hispano motor.

in the air. Each of them proved to be surprisingly successful. The Martin *MB1* bomber was not only ahead of any foreign war bomber but continued for years afterward to lead in its class. The Loening two-seater fighter—a new design of strut-braced monoplane—was lighter, faster, climbed higher and outflew the Bristol *Fighter* then in use at the front. The Vought and the Thomas-Morse also were far superior to their European rivals. All their guns and bomb racks worked.

While this was going on, General Squier was relieved of his post as head of the Aviation Section. The Army setup was altered by Presidential order, in May 1918. Gen. William L. Kenly became the Chief of the Department of Military Aeronautics of the Army, and Mr. John D. Ryan (a great mining industrialist) became head of the Bureau of Aircraft Production, with Potter as his aide. Thus, the old Signal Corps arrangement was abandoned for good, and the military had one head for air operations. The automotive influence had been removed, and for ample reason, as was evidenced by the two investigations necessitated by public clamor because of the abject failure of the air program. The first was the Military Affairs Committee of the Senate inquiry into the aircraft operations of the Army. The other, directed by President Wilson, was the investigation conducted by Supreme Court Justice Charles Evans Hughes, specifically "inviting scrutiny of the aircraft enterprises centered at Dayton, Ohio, and the activities of Edward A. Deeds and his former business associates."

Hughes' final recommendation did not find anyone actually guilty of fraud but did suggest that in the case of Deeds and Vincent, a court-martial procedure should be instituted to determine possible violations of military regulations. This never came to anything because Secretary of War Newton Baker declined to move in that direction. As to the Senate committee hearing, their principal conclusion on the first cause of the aircraft production fiasco was that "the airplane program was largely placed in the control of great automobile and other manufacturers who were ignorant of aeronautical problems."

The aircraft industry breathed a collective sigh of relief. It was clear that in Ryan and Potter, firm, straightforward managers, were at the helm of aircraft production, with no nonsense tolerated. A welcome air of efficiency replaced the semisecret finagling and favoritism that had existed with the auto leaders. By October 1918, production was rolling.

Potter had stopped all deliveries of *DH-4's* in August until every change asked for by the Air Force was complied with. By October a few *DH-4's* actually reached combat at the front. They were dubbed "flaming coffins," but they flew at least as well as or better than their British forebears. Production now assumed gratifying proportions. Between July 1 and October 1, 1918, 2,000 warplanes were built, about four times as many as in the entire previous year. In the same period, almost 8,000 Liberty motors were delivered and by the end of October, 150 motors a day were rolling off the lines. By way of comparison, in England the production of Rolls-Royce motors was only 10 a day. To this extent, the automobile people had finally done a good job.

A month before the armistice, Charles W. Nash, brilliant, forceful auto executive, took hold of production. His plans called for thousands of Martin bombers and Loening fighters, but they were never to mature because of the sudden end of the war. Some of us had an understandable feeling of disappointment, but these two planes, in particular, survived in the coming peace era. The huge production plans perhaps helped to frighten the Germans into an earlier armistice.

Assistant Secretary of War Benedict Crowell, in his detailed book, *America's Munitions,* referring to the aircraft production difficulties of World War I, asserted, "The fundamental difficulty of all these attempts was that we were trying to fit an American engine to a foreign airplane, instead of building an American airplane."

No American-designed airplane reached the land front in France, but to Curtiss must go the great credit of designing and producing in impressive quantity for the Navy the *HS2,*

This plane and the *H16* boat were the chief products of the air industry for the war. This is the famous *Jennie,* the Curtiss *JN4-D.*

H16, and later the *F5L* flying boats, which were so effective and successful in coast patrol and antisubmarine warfare all over the world.

At least one action generally beneficial to the entire aircraft industry (and particularly to the newly air-minded auto firms) occurred during this bewildering period. On July 24, 1917, the Manufacturers Aircraft Association was formed, with Samuel Bradley as general manager. The members were Wright Aeronautical Corporation (formerly Wright-Martin), Curtiss Aeroplane Company, Aeromarine Company (new Navy contractor), Standard Aircraft Company, the L. W. F. Company (laminated wood fuselage), and other large flying-machine builders, including the auto concerns (whose operations were so facilitated). The association was formed under considerable pressure from the National Advisory Committee for Aeronautics, from the Aircraft Board, and with the approval of the Secretary of the Navy and the Secretary of War, as well as the Attorney General. The purpose: to lay the Wright patent fight into a deep grave, never to rise again. The patent pooling, cross-licensing agreement involved was generous, paying several million dollars to pioneers like Wright. For the rest, all patents were placed in a pool so everyone could use them, paying the association a fee of $200 for each plane built. In due course, from this huge fund, distribution was made to patent owners who were paid on a scale commensurate with the value of their invention (determined by an impartial board). It has worked well down to the present day.

Summing up, Deeds and company were sincere enough in an effort to do a great job for the war and reap the profit. They would have richly deserved the profit if they had delivered to the front by January 1918 at least the first thousand acceptable *DH* planes instead of none. They did accomplish one objective. Dayton became and still is the technical center of military aviation.

Viewed from their record of accomplishment, if the American designers, after receiving the go-ahead, had been rushed to work on plans they had on paper in June 1917, instead of in February 1918, we very likely would have had some American planes (not copies) in action before the war ended. And perhaps we would have helped to shorten it.

It is about time for the factual aircraft production story to be told. At the start of war-aircraft production activities, the automotive groups in control presumed that they had the know-how for aircraft work. According to the Senate and Hughes investigations, they certainly did not. This was their undoing, lamentable and regretful as it was. Did they waste a lot of money? Not as much as generally attributed to them.

In many books, articles and reports, the harsh statement is often found, "One hundred and ninety-six planes for one billion dollars." This is neither justified, nor is it needed to point out the poor showing that was made.

The final accounting story is this, in round figures. The appropriations released by Congress from April 1917 to the November 1918 end of the war totaled $1,200,000,000. By the end of the period needed to close all accounts, $582,000,000 of this had been returned to the U.S. Treasury, and an additional $20,000,000 came back as payment for sales of surplus items. This leaves the sum of $598,000,000 as the real cost of all aircraft activities for that period. Of this, $139,000,000 was spent

Smithsonian's National Air and Space Museum

The Liberty motor, major success of our World War I production. It delivered 400 horsepower and weighed about 900 pounds, complete with water-filled radiator.

abroad to purchase 5,200 training and fighting planes, and 7,000 engines, plus fields, storehouses, etc. Then some $70,000,-000 was spent in the United States on testing, research, training fields, schools, and equipment of all kinds. In addition, balloons and dirigibles cost $7,000,000 more; miscellaneous guns, bombs, cameras, mounts, etc., about $25,000,000 more. This leaves us with a total of $357,000,000 spent for the manufacturing of 13,894 planes in America (mostly for training) and 41,953 engines, some 20,000 of which would be the "bank" of surplus engine material on which our secondhand-plane flyers and builders of many new planes would live for almost ten years. The total expenditure was not "a billion" at all, as was so widely proclaimed, but it was huge, to be sure, compared to the final result.

At the front on that last day of the war were a pitiful 196 American *DH-4* planes with Liberty motors—already obsolete when they got there. For observation or fighting, the pilot and gunner were separated and could not communicate. For bombing, their range was too short. Between the pilot and gunner was the gas tank—hence the name "flaming coffin" if a German incendiary bullet happened to hit in this unprotected region.

Disheartening it was . . . the American aircraft production war record.

7 War Surplus Blues

WITH the war ended, apprehension took hold of the aviation industry. Where now? . . . And with what money?

The automobile people had their profits, to be sure, but their desire to get back into mass production of cars far outweighed and overcame any plans or hopes they may have had of entering a doubtful airplane field. So one after another, the companies that had worked on aircraft or airplane engines closed their doors to flying ideas. First Ford, then Lincoln, Buick, Marmon, and General Motors got away from aviation as fast as they could. So did Fisher Body, Engel Aircraft, and many others making airframes or parts. Enough was enough. Their air headaches were over and in many companies such as Lincoln, new plants had been built for them that they could buy back cheaply from the Government. Scandal and criticism had left disillusionment, to be sure, but a select few of the automotive units did not share these sentiments. Packard stayed on for several years, although not very successfully. Dayton-Wright plugged along, too, for a while, but finally got discouraged with the unrewarding peacetime struggle. Ford was destined to return to aviation in a few years with a notable contribution.

The field was thus pretty well cleared of interlopers, and returned (for what it was worth) to the original entrepreneurs of prewar days. Aviation had grown neither "big" nor "fast" during the war period with any permanence. Deflation and the desire to crawl into a storm cellar was the mood of the day. Big business had no interest whatever in any future growth of flying. The great majority of released fighting aviators were so happy to get away from the rigors they had gone through, that large numbers of them (except for a few "gypsies," some ex-service flyers and young adventurers) were almost hostile to any further mention of flying. So, of course, were their families. For some of the pilots, though, time would change this feeling, and they would long to return to the air with no guns shooting at them.

Happily, in those dark days of 1919 there were some optimists. A few saw the peacetime potential of air travel. The two notable live-wire companies were Curtiss and Aeromarine. These outfits ploughed their war profits right back into the airplane development field.

Smithsonian's National Air and Space Museum
The *NC-4* in flight.

During the last year of the war, Glenn Curtiss had left the Buffalo complex and established at Garden City, Long Island, New York, a new unit separate from the Willys-led Curtiss companies. He called this unit the Curtiss Engineering Corporation. Here was assembled an engineering, research and designing staff headed by William L. Gilmore, ably assisted by George Page and Theodore Wright, all of whom were destined to continue making many important contributions to aircraft development. While the orders at the Buffalo plants tapered off rapidly after the armistice, the Garden City plant was to be the hatching place for a whole series of new developments, many of them on Government orders from the Navy.

The development most important for its significance and effect on the air industry's progress was the construction of the large *NC* flying boats. This design had already been laid out for the Navy under Adm. David Taylor's direction by two Naval constructors who were to contribute many vital engineering features and hull-design parameters to the lore of flying-boat building: Jerome C. Hunsaker and Holden C. Richardson. The *NC* stood for Navy-Curtiss. The Navy's order for four of these craft was fulfilled rapidly at the new Garden City Curtiss Engineering plant. The more or less secret objective for which these planes were being created was the Navy's plan to span the Atlantic Ocean by air for the first time in order to deliver by air (and not by sinkable cargo ships) planes so badly needed. The *NC* used four Liberty engines; its wings spanned 126 feet with an area of 2,380 square feet. The plane, loaded with 1,200 gallons of fuel and a crew of six, weighed 28,000 pounds; it was the heaviest that had yet been flown off the water. These giants were undergoing further testing in early May 1919, and I was privileged to be an observing passenger aboard the *NC-1* on an eight-hour nonstop flight. I thought it would never end. Its cruising speed was slow—80 to 85 miles an hour—and there was no shelter for "supercargoes" like me, and it was cold and windy almost beyond endurance for so long a time. No lunch either.

The Navy transatlantic unit was placed under the command of Comdr. John H. Towers on the *NC-3,* Lt. Comdr. P. N. L. Bellinger on the *NC-1,* and Lt. Comdr. A. C. Read on the *NC-4.* All three started from Rockaway, New York, before May 8. They left Trepassy, Newfoundland, on May 16 for the long transoceanic leg to the Azores. The *NC-1* and *NC-3* had trouble getting there, but the *NC-4* came through via Azores and Portugal, landing in the harbor of Plymouth amid great acclaim on May 31. A heroic incident was the 200 miles of taxiing in rough water that was done by the crew of the *NC-3*—a crew member riding on the right wing tip to balance the loss of the left wing pontoon.

On their own, the Curtiss engineers proceeded to design, build and fly a group of new types of aircraft. The *Model F* flying boat grew into a better-upholstered, four-seat version called the *Seagull,* with an almost automobile finish to appeal to the private owner. The speed was 80 miles per hour, and it could fly for two hours, reaching an altitude of 8,000 to 9,000 feet. The controls were handy, the stability as good as this type could be. Compared to many other aircraft of the day, it proved easy enough to fly. Many were sold, possibly 100, and went into worldwide use at a time when private flying was thought to be over with. For the land machine market, the Curtiss *Oriole* was brought out, a neat three-seater that won records and made nationwide demonstrations. For a still greater market a much larger passenger plane was developed, the Curtiss *Eagle*. This was a three-engine design carrying eight passengers in a comfortable enclosed cabin with low noise level, at a cruising speed of about 90 miles an hour. Many publicity stunts were done with it, but no airlines resulted.

There is no doubt that these and the others of the Curtiss peacetime fleet were far ahead of their time. While Curtiss had elaborate sales organizations around the country, there was no market large enough to justify the big expenditures that this bold development policy entailed. The public was not ready. There was still much distrust and widespread fear of flying except for a few sportsmen and forward-looking dreamers who ignored the mounting toll of "gypsy" flying fatalities featured by the press. The prevailing mood of the day was to go back to normalcy. But, in his book *Flying Squadrons*, S. Paul Johnston aptly points out, "Back to normalcy did not include Aviation."

Inglis Uppercu and his Aeromarine Company also showed great courage and determination in facing the rigors of passing from hectic war activities to the orderly-peacetime merchandising of a product. His approach was different from that of Curtiss. Aeromarine, with its neat-sized factory at Keyport, New Jersey, did little to bring out new types, but rather aimed at converting Navy seaplanes to passenger and cargo use, as well as acting as sales agent for surplus aircraft. Many were available at bargain prices, and Uppercu, after all, was the leading New York Cadillac distributor. He proceeded boldly to organize passenger and freight airlines to use the conversions his plant was working on—Navy flying boats in two sizes. The smaller was a three or four-seater *HS*, with an enclosed cockpit cabin cover. The larger boat was of the *F5L*, twin-Liberty-

Smithsonian's National Air and Space Museum

The Aeromarine flying boat developed from the Navy *F5L.*

engine Navy type. This one had real passenger cabin accommodations for eleven persons and was the best effort at an airliner in the U.S. up to this date.

With seven *F5L*'s in its fleet, plus several smaller ones, Aeromarine Airways, Inc., proceeded to set up passenger airlines from New York to Atlantic City, from Cleveland to Detroit, and principally from Key West to Havana—our first international air transportation attempt. Privately financed, this was quite different from foreign airline evolution. France, England, and Japan were all establishing government-subsidized air transport growth. Lines were established from London to Paris, Paris to Morocco, Tokyo to Japan's outer islands, and London to Australia. In England, 300,000 pounds had been voted for the Air Ministry; in Japan 400,000 yen; and in France over 2,000,000 francs. In the United States—nothing. Not even an Air Ministry, or any organization or regulation whatever for commercial aviation. Years away!

Showing persistence and skill, Aeromarine went ahead with their important but expensive pioneering. A total of 1,100 passengers in 1920 grew to 9,000 in 1922. Starting with three boats, they were operating twelve two years later. By December 1922, they had flown 1,000,000 miles and carried 17,000 passengers without a single mishap. But . . . oh, the overhead! For every $100 spent, 69 percent went to insurance, depreciation and sales promotion. Only 15 percent went to fuel and labor, and about 16 percent to maintenance. The insurance was prohibitive because of a lack of a regulatory federal law. In those days, engines were torn down completely every 100 hours of flight (now it is over 6,000 hours). In a final and very impressive sales pitch, the Aeromarine flying cruiser *Santa Maria,* with eleven passengers and crew, started from Key West on April 10, 1921, on an epic demonstration of flying. First to Miami, then to one city after another. Washington—New York—Albany—Montreal—Toronto—Buffalo—Detroit—Chicago, and on down the Mississippi to St. Louis, ending at New Orleans without an accident. At a time when there were so few airports, the ability of this flying boat to land at every city visited, right near the center of town (and en route having so many landing spots available in lakes and rivers), points up clearly that seaplanes and flying boats at that time had a strikingly important advantage over land planes. What reduced this advantage was the higher cost of maintenance and operation of waterbased craft, despite the fact that the Aeromarine pilots got only $90 a week and the mechanics $55 a week.

A year or so later it became evident that the high cost of this fine effort could not be met by the low-fare passenger revenue, and the Aeromarine lines faded out of the picture. A shame, because a relatively small Government subsidy, such as foreign lines were receiving, would have kept these American lines going until better, cheaper to maintain equipment would have put them in the black. One of Aeromarine's ablest pilots, Ed Musick, became an important Pan American Airways pioneer in later years. Congress had still to be awakened.

Other aircraft companies not only decided to stay with aviation but pretty much had to. Martin was the first to benefit from the slim Army Air Service appropriations available. In the background in military procurement from now on was the effective force of General "Billy" Mitchell. He had become Assistant Chief of the Army Air Service, and he had already laid plans for showing how hopelessly out of date were the Army General Staff officers in their appraisal of aviation. At this point, he was not so belligerent as he was later to become, but he was determined and foresighted. Therefore, the Army ordered 10 of Martin's superb *MB1* bombers. Donald Douglas had perfected their design. The Army ordered other planes, including a few Thomas-Morse single-seater fighters that were showing a speed of over 164 miles per hour (a record for that time). They were found so good that a year later, Boeing was awarded a low-bidder contract for 200 copies of the Thomas-Morse *MB3*—the first big contract that put Boeing in business. Some advanced training planes from Curtiss and Vought and a few Packard Le Peres (Liberty engine, special high-altitude two-seaters) were also purchased by the Air Service. Contracts for improved *DH-4*'s were also awarded.

I can state with particular emphasis that the Navy was not asleep either. Our Loening *Model M8 O* two-seater fighter, with the well-placed Lewis gun ring, appealed to the Marine Corps aviators who had tested it. And Commander E. O. McDonnell, a leading Naval aviator and technician, already deep in plans for an aircraft carrier along the lines the British were advocating, saw for this plane an immediate use. The result was a happy conclusion. The Navy ordered 83 Loenings.

The Loening Aeronautical Engineering Corporation sounded big, but its postwar plant consisted of a fifth-floor loft on West 52nd Street, in the heart of New York City. Typical of the airplane business, however, it had the best possible asset—a highly successful design, well drawn up, easy to produce, and patented. Flying samples performing in Dayton with the Army often broke records. For the Marines and for carriers the Navy needed landplanes. The *M8 O* would do. Because of the obviously limited facilities the Loening Company then had, this order was divided; the contract provided that 50 of the monoplanes would be built by the Naval Aircraft Factory in Philadelphia and the others by Loening. This meant a big increase in our operations, and the first thing I did was to prevail on my brother, Maj. Albert Palmer Loening of the Air Service, recently demobilized, to join me as vice-president and treasurer of our company, where he was to remain for the next decade. The small elevator in our cheap loft was, from then on, taxed to its limit, receiving Hispano motors from the Wright Company and subcontracted tail surfaces from the Aeromarine Company, as well as landing gears from the Curtiss Garden City plant. These had also been subcontracted. Down the same limited-capacity elevator, by some alchemy worked by Albert and our staff (Julie Holpit, John Laustra, Harry Larson, and others), there went out the sleek-looking *M8 O's*. Meanwhile, the other 50 planes were well on their way to completion at the Naval Aircraft Factory at the Philadelphia Navy Yard (which the Navy had used in the war period to build *HS* Curtiss flying boats, *F5L* boats, and many secret aeronautical devices). In charge of Loening production as assistant under Captain G. C. Westervelt, leading Naval aircraft constructor, was a young graduate of Cornell and the M.I.T. Navy School, Lt. LeRoy Randle Grumman. He did so good a job that after this contract work was finished, he was prevailed upon to resign from the Navy and come to the Loening Company as shop manager. In this capacity he continued for almost ten years.

These were the principal manufacturing activities under contract in the difficult years immediately following the end of the war. The *NC's* were rivaled promptly for the glory of conquering the Atlantic. Much of their glamour was taken away when the British team of John Alcock and Arthur Whitten Brown flew their Vickers *Vimy* bomber nonstop across the

Atlantic, 1,936 miles from St. Johns, Newfoundland, to the coast of Ireland in 16 hours on June 14, 1919 (instead of 23 days for the *NC-4*). Their plane was a modified war craft with two Rolls-Royce, 400-horsepower motors, 67 feet in span, 1,330 square feet in wing area, carrying 865 gallons of fuel and weighing 12,000 pounds gross. Most importantly, they won the *Daily Mail* prize of $50,000, the very one that Curtiss and Wanamaker had had their eyes on and for which the *America* flying boat had been built in 1914. Other efforts were made to cross the Atlantic in 1919, all unsuccessful except for the outstanding round trip of a British "lighter-than-air" airship, the huge *R-34*.

My first experience with the so-called "rigid" airships occurred when I happened to be at Roosevelt Field, Long Island, on July 6, 1919, to see the arrival of this giant after its crossing of the Atlantic. Of course there was much in the newspapers about this voyage. The *R-34* had left Pulham, England, on July 2, arriving over Roosevelt Field four days later. The speed of crossing was not too impressive, but the landing was. As the ship floated stationary over the field at an altitude of 1,000 feet, a sudden burst of white fell from its control cabin. In a moment the object opened into a parachute, and with a sangfroid and chic that only the English can put over, the executive officer of the *R-34*, Squadron Leader Pritchard, landed lightly and unconcerned, in full beribboned uniform, carrying a swagger stick! Efficiently he commanded the landing operations. Then a long process of warping the ship down to tie-downs, with the crew of thirty and several eager helpers holding on. I was able now to examine it quite closely; my first impression was how "unrigid" it really was. In photos and when first seen, it seemed a massively strong structure, justifying its name of "rigid." But close up, one was astonished to see how the frame squeaked, bent and shivered, with the cloth covering almost flapping in wind gusts. Many years later, when I was a member of the *Hindenburg* investigating board, more was to be learned about this type of construction. The next day a storm

Smithsonian's National Air and Space Museum

The British dirigible balloon, the *R-34*.

came up and again I was a witness. Lighter than air it certainly was. And the air knew it! I was shocked at its flimsiness and the wicked wrenching of the gusts. The wind gusts seemed so severe that the whole works seemed likely to be wrecked any moment. Frantically, the crew and many others tugged and pulled on ropes and handrails to restrain the monster in its unwieldy gyrations. As for the shivering and shaking of the "rigid" structure, it so shocked me that from that day on I could not put any faith in these slow, storm-vulnerable, expensive, and to me highly impractical "pigs." In my mind (as I left with no desire to see it again) were thoughts about the last futile *Zeppelin* raid on London. Twelve of them were caught by high winds and British fighting planes, and were completely routed, three falling to the ground; six blown over France, frozen and with no fuel left; two lost over the sea; and one limping back to its home. Also I remembered that wise saying of Louis Bleriot, "Slow aircraft have no *raison d'être*."

The *R-34* returned to England July 12, 1919, after a three-day crossing. In October, 1919, the U.S. Navy purchased a tragedy—the *R-38*, a sister ship, for $2,500,000. It was delivered to a U.S. crew the following year, and after a few proving flights it broke up and exploded, killing several people.

The ease with which the returned war aviator with adventurous spirit could buy surplus Army or Navy planes for a few hundred dollars each was the reason aviation became associated for years in the public mind with unacceptable danger. There was no regulatory or pilot licensing procedure. The "gypsy" flyers had their heyday in the early twenties. Let us not minimize their value. Clyde Cessna, Walter Beech, Walter Varney, Jack Frye, and Charles Lindbergh were but a few of these early "birdmen" who toured the country, picking up money to live on or excitement to keep up their spirits by "barnstorming" any field, carrying passengers for a few dollars or doing stunts, looping, wing-walking at fairs. Many of them became designers and builders of famous aircraft and presidents of great airlines. There were "good" gypsies, to be sure, serious, skillful flyers. But many, too many of their confreres died in crashes that were due principally to pilot error! These had no right to be flying. In 1921, of 114 accidents there were 49 fatalities, and the next year 62. In what little strictly commercial flying existed, such as the Aeromarine and Curtiss operations, there were only 6 fatalities for twice as many hours in the air, and none of them due to pilot error.

This continuous series of accidents the gypsy flyers were piling up, with accompanying newspaper headlines, was depressing enough. But now came a new blow in the struggle the aircraft business was waging to acquire the confidence of the public, bankers, and passengers.

George Houston, president of the Wright Aeronautical Corporation (in 1919 they had changed from the Wright-Martin name), called me to his office in early May 1920, and there disclosed a daring plan of the British aircraft industry. Houston, who had been a partner of General George Goethals, had an exceptionally clear-thinking engineering mind. He saw right through the project and unhesitatingly devised means to stop it.

Handing me some printed advertising material, he explained that the British were wise enough to know that with our lack of any licensing or regulations, they could dump their old war stuff on our market, with no duty to pay, and a lot of "credulous saps" would buy this junk, at such low prices that even our Army surplus boys couldn't compete. This would, indeed, be a severe blow to the industry, and would make our accident rate soar even more.

Glancing at the printed matter, I learned that the "Aircraft Disposal Corporation" of England was going to exhibit at an "Aeroshow" at the Steel Pier at Atlantic City, and that they were offering "Aeroplanes At Last for the Aviators" (of all types, from the old *F.E. 26* pusher model to the Sopwith *Salamander* and the Vickers *Vimy* of transatlantic fame). Also offered were "Engines at Attractive Prices for the Manufacturer" of makes from all sources—Rolls-Royce, Gnome, Hispano, and to add insult to injury, the Liberty. Everything was stated as "Brand New! With prices F.O.B. New York: delivery June 1, and with a large quantity of spares available to keep all planes and engines in constant service at small cost."

Looking up at Houston, I found him smiling and shaking his head as he proceeded. "How about that? . . . . Now you get right down to Atlantic City and give these old war relics a close look. I want you to check if they are dangerous to sell to our boys, and if you feel they are, send a telegram of protest to Senator New and to the Ways and Means Committee of the House. Then we will give this to the press here. Meanwhile, other steps are being taken to put a crimp in Mr. William H. Workman and send him back about his business." Workman was the agent and representative of Handley-Page, the head of this syndicate that had bought 10,000 surplus British planes for resale in America.

Immediately, I went to the Atlantic City Steel Pier where this "aircraft show" was in progress. Carefully I inspected the planes, with Mr. Workman not too happy about it. Many fittings had rusted from improper storage, careless overseas shipment, or saltwater exposure. Besides, some of these planes, such as the Sopwith *Dolphin* and the *DH-10,* were still somewhat experimental and known to be tricky to fly. All of them except the *Avro* would be dangerous on our typical small farm pasture fields. So I sent this telegram:

> Have completed inspection of obsolete British war-surplus planes offered for sale on our market, by the Aircraft Sales Corporation of London. Regardless of effect of such wholesale dumping on our industry these planes are mostly unairworthy, rendered dangerously uncertain in many details by age and overseas shipment, requiring special flying ability for safety. If such aircraft are permitted to enter country, ensuing accidents would be responsibility of Government agency with power to halt this wholesale dumping.

The press picked this up. While the Senate still dawdled, *The New York Evening Post* of June 2, 1920, said under the editorial heading, "Aid For Our Aircraft Industry":

> There is little question that the plans to bring in thousands of British machines at very low prices would soak up the little domestic demand which exists. . . . In a telegram to the House Ways and Means Committee, which has had protective legislation under consideration, Grover Loening has said that the question of whether the dumping of foreign planes would break down the industry was secondary to the responsibility which rested on Congress to protect the American public from the use of machines

> "rendered dangerously uncertain by age and overseas shipment". . . . Protection of the industry is essential for commercial and defensive purposes.

The House of Representatives committee had taken it up already on May 28 in hearings on the bill prepared by Rep. John Q. Tilson of Connecticut. At these hearings, witnesses were all in favor of restrictive legislation, including not only the aircraft people but leaders of the services. General Billy Mitchell became the star witness when he said, "If this market is flooded with this English equipment, it will practically knock out the possibility of our defending ourselves in the air in war. You will be turning over the key to the front door to some other nations." Others had joined in with similar statements. The press had urged, "America First." The Tilson Bill was passed unanimously by the House in record time. The bill was known to have the overwhelming support of the Senate, but the 66th Congress drew to a close before it could act. So Congress failed.

Then George Houston drew his trump card—the Wright patent. The Wright Aeronautical Corporation at once entered suit for an injunction prohibiting these sales. After hearings first by Judge T. I. Chatfield in the U. S. District Court in Brooklyn, and then by Judge Mayer of the U. S. District Court in New York City, the injunction was granted. The court threw out the contention of the British that the planes had been licensed in England.

The "dumping" enterprise ended right there.

Though we were still not to have that needed regulation and pilot licensing for several years, progress stumbled along without it. In addition to having a few "good" gypsies, there were other tremendously helpful influences in the further advancement of practical and useful aviation. The small but effective Government orders to the industry meant much, indeed.

But, perhaps even more significant were two vital stimulants —the Air Mail . . . and General Billy Mitchell.

Smithsonian's National Air and Space Museum

Immediately after World War I one of the most important developments in the American air industry was the successful radial air-cooled engine designed and perfected by "Charlie" Lawrance. When Lawrance merged with Wright Aeronautical, this engine grew into the famous, still widely used Whirlwind. Lawrance ranks with Wright and Curtiss as one of the great pioneers of American aircraft development.

8 The Mail Takes to the Air

NEITHER snow nor rain . . . nor gloom of night stays these swift couriers . . ." from carrying the mail from coast to coast across this vast country—but a balky or unreliable engine could!

That is why we must give ample credit for success in the pioneer undertakings of the twenties to the improved reliability of the surplus engines that the U.S. aircraft industry had to use. This is the way it had to be worked out.

Thousands of Liberty engines were left over from excess war production. If the war had lasted for two or more years longer, this would have been a shocking waste. War requirement changes would surely have rendered them obsolete. In fact, just before the war's end, a much more suitable aircraft engine, the ABC 300-horsepower, fixed nine-cylinder radial, had appeared in England. Lawrance Aero Engine Company in the United States had on paper the great engine that was to conquer so many air problems in the ensuing decade—the Whirlwind nine-cylinder, 200-horsepower radial. This type is used even to this day, and has since been developed into different sizes and models. The real American pioneer of the fundamentally correct engine designed from the start, particularly for airplane use, was Charles Lanier Lawrance. He has received too little credit for his creation. The Whirlwind's many feats included pounding away faithfully for thirty-three hours without a miss in its *Spirit of St. Louis* mounting, drawing Lindbergh snug, in his seat behind it, for those thrilling 3,600 miles across the endless, wet-looking Atlantic.

At a Lindbergh celebration banquet years later, Lawrance dismissed his dearth of fame by the comment, "Who remembers the name of Paul Revere's horse?"

New, advanced motors for airplanes faced a discouraging future for those few years after the war ended. The huge Government stocks were there . . . so easy to buy for prices ever lower and more tempting. There were not only the Liberties, but also vast stocks of that cherished training engine, the Curtiss OX-5. This engine was to remain dear to the hearts of thousands of flying cadets and the surviving barnstormers. Two generations later, the aficionados of this venerable eight-cylinder, water-cooled, 90-horsepower motor have a strong organization, based on nostalgia, meeting with various degrees of hilarity all over the country—the "OX-5 Clubs."

There were other engines struggling for acceptance on the planes of the early twenties. Kinner and Warner radials began to appear, with five and seven cylinders, giving about 90 to 120 horsepower. The Aeromarine factory had developed a series of water-cooled engines, but the Liberty rivalry was too much for them.

Curtiss came on the scene with a very formidable line of six and twelve-cylinder motors based first on the designs of Charles Kirkham, and finally developing in 1922 into the Curtiss D-12 designed by Arthur Nutt. This was a highly successful 400-horsepower motor and won races, established records, and finally proved useful in new Army pursuit airplanes. The Wright Aeronautical Company had continued to develop newer and larger water-cooled engines from the 300-horsepower Hispano to the 600-horsepower Tornado. Numerous

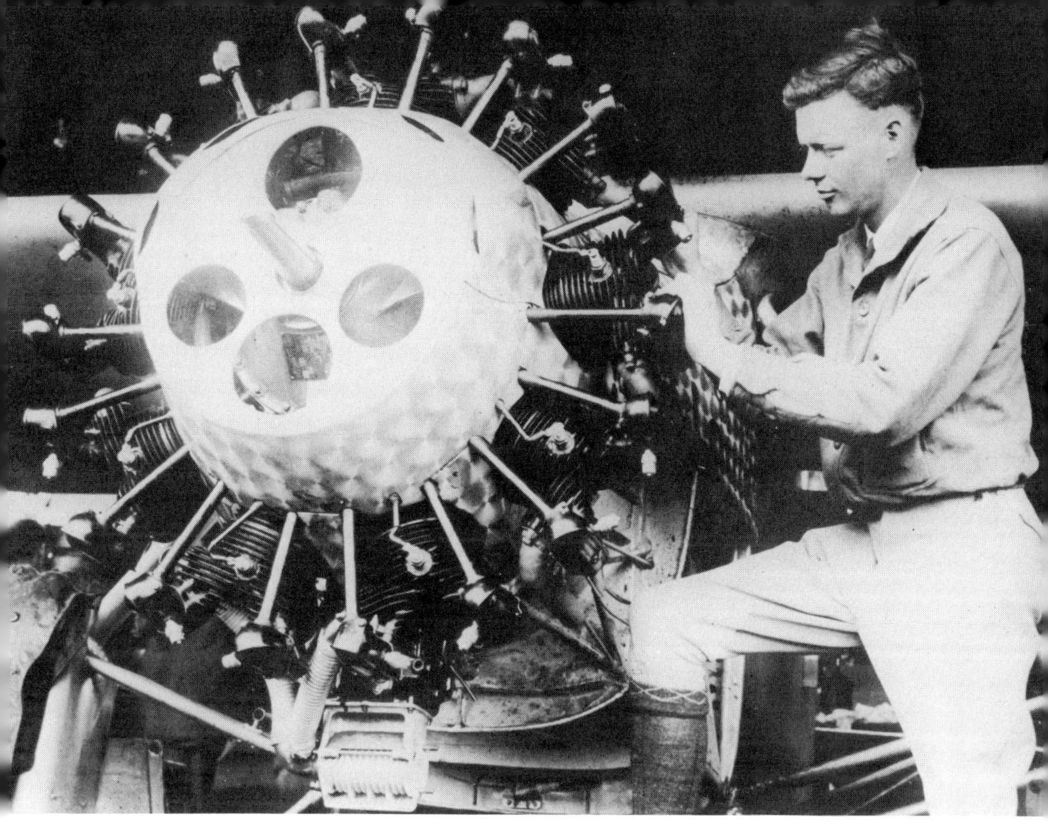

Smithsonian's National Air and Space Museum

The Wright Whirlwind motor being examined by Charles Lindbergh. On his Paris flight this engine delivered up to 223 horsepower at 1,800 revolutions per minute. It weighed 500 pounds.

surplus planes in commercial flying stuck by the old war type 150-horsepower Wright-Hispano that joined the Liberty and the OX-5 in wide usage. Packard Auto Company also continued developing their engines, including a twelve-cylinder, water-cooled, 600-hosepower version in 1922. Much was expected of this motor, but little actual success was achieved with it other than in fast boats.

The bulk of the really important flying operations for two or three years after the armistice depended on the Liberty engine —early maligned because of the ridiculous publicity story of its birth that the auto people, who fathered it, were stupid enough to broadcast. This was the yarn that two engineers, J. G. Vincent and E. J. Hall, locked themselves in a hotel room for a week, lived only on cigarettes and coffee, and suddenly came forth with the designs of the great Liberty motor with which to win the war. What they really did come out with, after a hard-working session, was an inferior engine with eight cylinders that showed up so badly on the test stand that the War Aircraft Production Board had to form a committee of the best American experts to help rescue it from failure. D. McCall White of Cadillac, Henry Crane of Wright (Simplex-Hispano), O. E. Hunt of Chevrolet, and several others literally redesigned the motor. It was made into twelve cylinders with a new bearing and crankshaft combination; most important, the oiling system was changed from a scupper splash type, highly unsuitable for a high-compression aircraft motor, to a forced-feed, dry-sump type. This type of oiling system was also needed for a fighter plane to allow for all kinds of maneuvers—a condition which the original designers had not even thought of. So when the smoke cleared away and real production was started, the Liberty was a sound 400-horsepower, twelve-cylinder motor as fine as the Mercedes or the Rolls. There is no denying that the production planning of this engine to be built in great quantity was far ahead of anything the Europeans were capable of. The Detroit system was ahead on this, all right—but perhaps too far ahead. Ford was making cylinders at such a rate that it would have taken years to train enough aviators to fly enough planes to use them if production had not been stopped. But so many Liberty motors were completed about 12,000 of them later became available for surplus sales. At first, prices ranged from $1,800 to $3,000 apiece, but in a year or so the price dropped, and of course secondhand motors soon were selling (often to rum runners) for only a few hundred dollars apiece.

Congress was in a money-saving mood, so that whenever funds were requested for the purchase of motors, reluctant legislators referred back to the well-known stockpile of Liberties. Thus aviation operations of the Government, from 1919 and for many years thereafter, hinged on the Liberty

Smithsonian's National Air and Space Museum

The Air Mail Service steadily improved the Liberty engine. The only radical modification in the 1920 to 1925 period was the introduction of the inverted type. This improvement, engineered by Fred Heckert for the U.S. Air Service, was used for a few years until radial air-cooled engines swept the field.

motor. And because it was so cheap, so did most commercial operations. Aeromarine used the Liberty on their passenger flying boats. Several designers of new aircraft, including Loening, used them too, in order to increase sales to the services. Many improvements were made on the Liberty as it came into wider use. Its reliability became proverbial, and most of the great American air explorations and record flights in the five years after the war were made with Liberty motors.

The forced-feed lubrication system allowed for one of the most distinctive improvements, making the Liberty more adaptable to airplane design. The Liberty had always been difficult to install without blocking the vision of the pilot. The automobile engineers who had designed it were so used to the requirement for road clearance that they made the crankshaft position as near to the base of the engine as possible. But in aircraft, with the high tractor propeller mounted directly on the crankshaft, any engine parts above this shaft line impaired the pilot's view forward. Thus, the whole plane had to be raised to give the propeller its clearance, or the seat raised to permit visibility over the engine. With forced-feed, dry-sump lubrication, it was relatively simple to turn the Liberty upside down with the crankshaft on top, giving excellent clearance for the prop and for the pilot's front view. This was done with great success by the Army's motor engineer, Frederic Heckert, at the McCook Field, Dayton, shops. Immediately the entire air industry realized that all aircraft engines should have been that way from the start. Here was a typical instance of how habits or prejudices from one field are carried over to another, where they make no sense. In later years several motors, like the Fairchild Ranger, were built with the shaft at the top—correctly designed for propeller clearance and visibility requirements of an airplane instead of for road clearance of an automobile. The widest use of this inverted Liberty was in the Loening amphibian of 1924 to 1930—the plane used by the Army in the successful pioneer flight around South America.

Serious usefulness of airplanes was demonstrated in Europe, particularly in France and England, as soon as the war ended. Passenger line operations were Government-subsidized. London to Paris was the first outstanding route. As long as the Government made up the deficits, the lines prospered—or more exactly, were kept running at a great expense—excused and justified as a war safeguard. But the United States had no such subsidies and no inclination on the part of Congress or the public to vote them. Fortunately, the Army Air Service during the war had conceived the policy that some exigent, regularly scheduled flying would be good training for Army pilots and their equipment. An Air Mail Service in cooperation with the Post Office Department was inaugurated on May 15, 1918. Using the Curtiss *JN-4H* Hispano-engine planes, an Army unit was organized under the command of Maj. Reuben Fleet (who later was to become the founder of Fleet Aircraft Company and then the huge Consolidated Aircraft Company of World War II).

Smithsonian's National Air and Space Museum

Scene at Potomac Park, Washington, D.C., May 15, 1918, when the Air Mail Service was started by the Army with a Curtiss *JN-4H* airplane.

Operations began from Washington to New York. The New York terminal was at the inner field of the Belmont Park Racetrack, where racing fans of following generations were to read on a monument that at this popular concourse, America's huge air transport development had started in 1918. In Washington, the mail was landed in Potomac Park, at first, and then was moved to the small College Park field.

The first day's operation showed that this type of training was, indeed, very much needed. The pilot, Lt. G. H. Boyle, leaving Washington for New York, took off and, to the consternation of the V.I.P. inaugural crowd, headed straight southeast, landing, quite lost, at Waldorf, Maryland! An even more mortifying moment had occurred at the start when refusal of the trusted Hispano to start up was traced to an empty gas tank. Of course, it must be remembered that in those days the only instruments were a compass, a clock and an altimeter.

Seven years later, the American technique of cross-country

flying had been developed by the U. S. Air Mail Service to the highest degree of any such operation in the world, and gave this nation a practical grasp of commercial flying that has never been rivaled.

A short three months after its beginning, responsibility for the moving of mail was transferred from the Army to the Post Office, and the operation of this difficult use of aircraft became a separate Government activity. There were behavioristic, valid reasons for this in addition to desirable bureaucratic ones. An Army pilot was trained to accomplish his mission regardless of consequences. Hence, many wrecks. The commercial pilot, on the other hand, had to come through on time but without wrecking his valuable plane or cargo.

When the Post Office took over, the service between New York and Washington carried a mail load of 200 pounds per trip and used six planes for two daily round trips via Philadelphia. Then the operation began to grow. First, a daylight run was set up between New York and Cleveland. This was the most severe route and remained so for many years—the "graveyard" run through rain, fog, and high winds over the treacherous Allegheny Mountains. From Cleveland the mail was transferred to trains for Chicago and points farther west. Next, flying from Chicago to Omaha was established in May 1920. From there the mail proceeded to San Francisco by train.

Although by this method delivery of mail was expedited to the Pacific Coast by about a day, the transcontinental ambitions of the Postal Service were not realized. There was a missing link. The enterprising staff of Assistant Postmaster General Praeger and his superintendent, J. E. Whitbeck, spurred on first by the inspired zeal of Postmaster General Albert S. Burleson of Woodrow Wilson's Cabinet and then by Harding's Postmaster General, Will Hays, proceeded to forge it. By the spring of 1923, a lighted airway had been established between Cheyenne and Chicago, and lights between Cleveland and New York, Cleveland and Chicago, Cheyenne and Salt Lake City were later completed (adding to the daytime visual-marker

Smithsonian's National Air and Space Museum

The modified *DH-4* made into a highly successful mail plane. The pilot sat back of the gas tank and the mail compartment.

system), so that by July 1924, the completed lighted and daytime airway across the continent, with radio installations at all the main stations and thirty-four emergency fields, was ready for use. Two hundred and eighty-nine flashing beacons that weather could not stop beckoned their unerring invitation to the sky traveler, coaxing him to within sight of the next beam beyond, and so . . . to the coast. Little wonder that for this tremendously important contribution to the extension of safer air travel for everyone in America the Collier Trophy—the most coveted award in aviation—was given to the U.S. Air Mail Service for two years in succession, 1922 and 1923, "for the greatest achievement in aviation in America, the value of which has been thoroughly demonstrated by actual use during the preceding year."

Regular coast-to-coast service for delivery of mail or parcel post in a short 26 to 29 hours, instead of four or five days, started on July 1, 1924. The planes used were the de Haviland *DH-4* requisitioned from Army storage. By the time the Air Mail engineers at the well equipped Maywood, Illinois, Repair Facility got through with them, they were a far different plane than those of World War I vintage. The mail load carried was 500 pounds; the speed, 130 miles per hour. Some eighty of these planes constituted the Air Mail fleet. All other types, several of which had been ordered experimentally, had given way to a standardization that was the keynote of an efficient operation at the lowest possible cost. The only change needed to perfect the *DH-4* for load carrying over the high Rocky Mountain passes was to apply higher lift and more efficient wings, some of which were furnished successfully by the Loening Aeronautical Engineering Corporation's busy new factory on the East River in New York City.

A year and a half after the transcontinental Air Mail had started, at the end of 1925, here was the result: 3,800,000 miles had been flown, over a third at night. Over 16,000,000 letters had been carried, on which more than $1,000,000 had been collected in Air Mail surcharge. The record of safety was high, indeed, with only 0.02 percent of the letters lost due to accident.

The ice had been broken on the business use of aviation, by a Government-sponsored operation. It reflected the highest credit on Post Office Department directors and wide public recognition of the skill, tenacity, often heroism and dedication, shown by the wonderful group of mail pilots who did the job. One of the most pleasing parts of this history is that no breath of scandal was incident to this great effort, which was made in the middle of what should have been a devastating slump.

The Liberties had kept running. The success of the Air Mail operation now attracted, at last, a little interest from private enterprise. A feeble but insistent cry went up on the desirability of turning over the Air Mail operation to private contractors to be paid by the Post Office, much as was being done with the railroads. The Coolidge Administration and the Post Office went along with such proposals. General Mitchell joined in by advocating that such a move would encourage the establishment of airlines, which would be a desirable background for defense. Actually, they would be subsidized by the mail payments, giving as effective assistance as was being provided in Europe by direct Government aid to airlines that had created their justifiable buildup for national defense. The aircraft industry joined in advocating this and as a result, Congress passed the first Air Mail Law in 1925, a bill sponsored by Representative Clyde Kelly, known for years as the "Kelly Bill." Its wording constituted the Magna Carta of air transport, saying, "An act to encourage commercial aviation and to authorize the Postmaster General to contract for air mail service." At last we had Government aid—but still no regulation or licensing law.

In due course, contracts were entered into. The last flight of the Post Office operation was made on September 9, 1927, some nine years after its modest beginning. The total cost to the Government, through all these years, was $17,500,000 and $5,000,000 had been produced in mail revenue. What this great development did for immediate airline progress is found in the following year's statistics, which show 25,000 miles of Government-improved airways, 14,000 of them lighted with beacons at 1,000 airports. A short two years after the Kelly Bill gave commercial flying its start, aviation had grown to a total of 6,400 planes in use (mostly private and gypsy), with airlines using about 200 of them. Forty years later there would be 2,000 airline planes and 90,000 used in private and commercial flying.

The old Liberties had done their work well. They gave way presently to the new radial, air-cooled engines mounted on newer and faster planes that were gradually developing passenger accommodations. Thus we enter the American air transport era, so definitely started by the Air Mail Service of the Post Office.

Smithsonian's National Air and Space Museum

In the first few years after World War I, Billy Mitchell greatly advanced American aviation technique. His quarrels with his superiors were unfortunate and, toward his end, not very productive, but his part in the march into greatness of air development is undeniable.

9 Billy Mitchell and the Records

BRIGADIER GENERAL William Mitchell, son of a Wisconsin Senator from Milwaukee, was not a West Pointer. He is remembered chiefly for his persistent fight to free the Air Service from the old-line General Staff, the "groundhogs," as some liked to call them because of the stuffy way they looked upon aviation. There was a difference about aviation that puzzled and discomfited the old guard of the Army and Navy. Never had they dealt with such a tricky publicity situation as the glamour and mystery of flying generated. And Billy Mitchell was a master propagandist who knew how to use his opportunities. So they were losing out to Mitchell very rapidly in the press. The public read avidly all of Mitchell's outbursts about how aviation changed the course of war. The word went around Washington to stop this madman, at all costs, before he really upset things. It was thought best to keep him where he could be watched and even disciplined. Therefore, he was made Assistant Chief of the Air Service, first under General C. T. Menoher and then under its new Chief, General Mason F. Patrick. The latter was not as dead set against Mitchell as most people thought, because he had acquired a liking and respect for airplanes in war, and he encouraged in a fatherly way the young, eager engineers of the industry. He okayed many proposals that fellow enthusiasts of Mitchell's advanced to help develop aircraft design. Thus, when Mitchell and his highly competent assistants proposed new ways of showing the world, the U. S. Congress, and incidentally, the General Staff (if they were awake), what great things the airplane could do, Patrick went along, frequently to everyone's surprise.

A series of wonderful accomplishments by the Army Air Service took place with a rush as soon as the peacetime regime became established. Thus we find that Mitchell's value in developing the aircraft industry was far greater in visualizing and accomplishing air feats, and in pushing for records, than in his running battle for a "separate Air Force"—which he never got anyway. To the air industry, in the years 1919 to 1925, General Mitchell was a priceless stimulant, and he influenced enormously advances that the American industry made in its rivalry with Europe and in its battle to excite the business interest of the U. S. financial community.

Mitchell's feuding over Army air organization with his superiors and with Congress may have hurt aviation's orderly progress by alienating powerful forces. On the other hand, his organizing ability and drive actuated so many electrifying projects between 1919 and 1925, that perhaps he should have been awarded all the Collier Trophies that we had. Outstanding flying demonstrations and feats took place under his direction, or at least with his approval from the back room, all done at a time when American business offered no help, having had little if any venture capital to throw away on anything as unrewarding as the flying-machine business—which they believed was dead once the war was over. These feats and new developments were accomplished despite the niggardly appropriations from a hesitant Congress, tiny compared to what European nations were advancing to build up their commercial passenger networks aimed so frankly at building a base for warplane strength.

The first important demonstration by Mitchell's forces was engineered under the guise of the transcontinental air race. The start was October 8, 1919, from Mineola, New York, and the race was run jointly by the War Department and the American Flying Club. The Army planes were assigned under Mitchell's direction for pilot training, and this function was certainly served. The race was to be a round trip to the Pacific Coast and back—a distance of 5,400 miles. Forty-nine planes took off from Mineola and fourteen from San Francisco, mostly in Liberty-motored rebuilt and improved *DH-4's* and Hispano-motored Curtiss *JN-4H's*. The winner took nine days for the round trip, flying about fifty hours, making stops every 100 to 200 miles. Most of the entrants finished at least one leg; many had quite serious accidents. The contestants covered 124,777 miles. The race served as a grueling test of the readiness of the Air Service for serious work, in moving planes from one coast to the other and in laying out the transcontinental air route. A vast amount of technical information was obtained, on weather, on the need for radio, lights, more airfields, better maps, etc. The public was excited by this lively contest, and the papers gave it a lot of space. The Liberties showed up well, but the only engine that came through without the slightest adjustment or replacement was the Wright Hispano. While there was no immediate result in advancing the status of the air business, this eye-opening "derby" surely alerted many persons to the possibilities as well as the dangers of air travel. That's what Billy Mitchell hoped for.

The next Army achievement was the flight from New York to Nome, Alaska, executed by eight U. S. Army flyers with four airplanes under the command of one of Mitchell's most able aides, Lt. St. Clair Streett. This difficult and completely uncharted round trip took from July 15 to August 24, 1920. The Liberty *DH*'s used stood the rigors of the trip, and much was learned at this early date about Arctic conditions. Prior to this flight, Streett had been doing pioneer work in making up airways maps for general use; but particularly for Mitchell's own

U.S. Air Force

The *Ostfriesland* under attack.

eager beavers, who, like so many others then flying, got lost dangerously often. In connection with this helpful civilian service, the Army in February 1921 inaugurated a "model airway" from Washington to Dayton, Ohio. This operated on a regular schedule, and in the years before we were able to generate commercial passenger lines such as the extensive ones in Europe, the model airway fanned out to Army fields and stations from Kelly Field, Texas, to Selfridge Field, Detroit. By 1923 this operation had grown to three or four hundred thousand miles a year flown by Army and Navy aircraft. The airway provided a study of what was needed to make this form of transport a real utility. Also, it trained pilots in cross-country flying under strict regulations and scheduling, and tested new navigation instruments. Radio systems, lighting, and the requirements of weather forecasting, as well as an efficient transportation medium for Air Service personnel were developed. A twelve-seat model of the twin Liberty Martin bomber was developed for this purpose. In three years of operation of this model airway, no casualties or injuries to personnel assigned to the scheduled flying had resulted. Experts, backed by equally expert mechanics, with Mitchell pushing them and raising Cain if they did badly.

As June 1921 approached, the seething battle between Mitchell and all the service and Congressional bigwigs (who had been trying to hold him down and stop his propagandizing, or at least to reduce its effectiveness) came to a head. Mitchell had been writing articles, making speeches and testifying at hearings in the Capitol, reiterating and driving home his campaign for air power.

The Germans had ceded to the United States several of the finest warships the German Navy had used in the war. The condition attached was that they were to be used only for experimental purposes and were to be destroyed by August 1921. Among them was the "unsinkable" giant battleship of 28,000 tons, the *Ostfriesland.* Mitchell for years had been claiming that he could sink this ship and any others with air bombing if given a chance. But all kinds of tactics had been used to forestall this test. The high command of the Navy did not feel happy at taking this risk. "Mitchell might be just lucky enough," thought some, while many others just scoffed at such a preposterous idea. They planned to sink the German ships by gunfire. The Army didn't like it either, and in the Congress were several Senators and Representatives who joined in upbraiding Mitchell for wild talk. They were, perhaps, aware that if he succeeded in this daring project, it might involve quite a setback for some great armament industries. So he had to battle hard and bitterly against the prevailing Washington sentiment. Mitchell found important believers in his case—including Adm. William S. Sims, who commanded the Navy war forces in Europe, and Adm. Bradley Fiske, who himself was something of a rebel, vigorously advocating the development of torpedo-carrying planes. What was more important, Billy Mitchell had won over large segments of the press. Newspapers began insisting that the proposed bombing tests be conducted.

If these great and expensive "dreadnaughts" were really

"sitting ducks for bombers rather than our first line of defense," as Mitchell and so many aviators proclaimed, here was the chance to find out. So the opposition to this vital experiment was overcome mainly by the attitude of the press and public opinion. All kinds of last-minute moves were made to hamstring Mitchell. Even his chief, General Menoher, succumbed to pressure from the General Staff. A few weeks before the tests, Menoher claimed that Mitchell, by advocating a united and separate air force, in public statements, had violated the propriety and regulations under which he was appointed. Menoher requested the Secretary of War to remove him from office. Billy was not removed—the press bitterly denounced any such action. Finally, orders were issued for the bombing tests to be held on several days beginning July 13, 1921, with rules and limitations slipped in by the Navy to hamper success as much as possible, such as staging the affair far too far out at sea—75 miles off the Virginia Capes.

Not only Mitchell but all dedicated military aviators were on trial, and the world watched to see the outcome of this major test for the protection of a nation. The rest is well known history. The Army Air Service, under Mitchell's inspired direction, assembled as if for war at nearby Langley Field. For weeks the most expert engineers, armorers and mechanics groomed the fleet of new, improved Martin *MB5* bombers. The pilots practiced for days on some old hulks at the shore. Mitchell persuaded the Ordnance Department to devise and have specially made some 2,000-pound bombs (somewhat secretly to have up his sleeve).

On the first day of the tests, a destroyer was sunk in 19 minutes by 300-pound bombs. A few days later, the cruiser *Frankfurt* resisted the light bombs, but when 600-pounders were dropped on her, she survived for only 35 minutes. Then came the big and final day—attacks on the *Ostfriesland.*

On board the Army transport *Henderson* a group of guests was invited to witness the proceedings. Included were Secretary of War John Weeks, Secretary of the Navy Edwin Denby,

U.S. Air Force

The great battleship succumbs to the plane.

members of Congress, diplomats, foreign airplane observers, high-ranking officers, many members of the press and a group of aeronautical persons, including myself.

On July 21 the bomb explosion "that was heard around the world" took place. On the morning of that day, preliminary tests with some of the 1,000-pound bombs inflicted considerable damage to the superstructure of the battleship, but in the opinion of the umpires the vessel was still seaworthy. This did not worry the aviation people aboard, because we knew what Billy Mitchell had in reserve. In the afternoon the formation of eight special Martin bombers carrying the 2,000-pounders appeared (violating their time schedule, the Navy claimed). There had been among us a good deal of argument about the effectiveness of bombs landing in the water alongside the hull, as against direct hits. I was on the "direct hit crashing through the deck" wagon and bet accordingly. One direct hit did go down a stack and probably wrecked the interior. The operation was very noisy and the huge booms could be heard and felt on the *Henderson* hundreds of yards away. Most of the bombs were aimed at and did land in the water alongside the hull, with huge geysers of spray. A short twenty minutes after this heavy attack had started, the powerful-looking battleship began to look very sick, down some at the stern and listing to one side. Then after what could only be called a last bomb *coup de grâce*, down she went stern first, the bow rising in the air, showing great wounds in the hull as she slid under, only gurgles of spray and foam marking her grave.

A short while after this spectacle, a triumphant Mitchell in a fast plane flew very close by the deck of the *Henderson* with his white scarf flying, waving to all in a gesture not unmindful of the knights of old, to the chagrin of the "unsinkable battleship" boys and to the joy of all of us in the airplane business!

There followed a period of "explanations" and alibis by the Navy and by a host of Mitchell "scoffers." The battleship "was not in motion . . . it had no air protection . . . no antiaircraft guns to ward off the bombers . . ." and so on. The principal effect beneficial to the airplane industry was to wake up the Navy even more to the importance of incorporating aircraft into the fleet in a major way.

The Navy Bureau of Aeronautics had just been created. Its leader was Adm. William A. Moffett, ably assisted by Capt. John H. Towers, Adm. Emory Land, and Naval Constructor Hunsaker. They had no use for Billy Mitchell as a rival airpower advocate, but they secretly admired and often helped him. The aircraft industry now saw the buildup of its second major customer as the Navy began placing emphasis on aircraft carriers. They would be needing many, many new planes for the carriers and larger planes for patrol, bombing and torpedoing enemy fleets. The Navy air boys, too, had their troubles with dense and slow higher commands, but there is little doubt that they were helped by Mitchell's torch-bearing without being tarred with the same brush. The Navy's preoccupation with the *Zeppelin* rigid airship developments, that was to prove so frustrating and so useless in the end, had retarded their airplane advancement, but they soon caught up.

Despite his victory Mitchell and his able staff—at that time Col. T. DeWitt Milling, Col. Thurman Bane, Maj. "Toohey" Spaatz, Maj. "Mike" Kilner, Maj. Reuben Fleet, Maj. Robert Olds, Capt. Ira Eaker, and Capt. Burdette Wright to name a few—did not in the flush of success forget that the weak and still struggling aircraft industry needed more demonstrations of its tremendous possibilities. So they continued to build up impressive feats one after the other.

The 1909–1912 exhibition and prize era was vitally important to airplane advancement. The World War I era did much for production but not so much for design. The war period was dull on development and long on scandal. But the 1920 to 1925 period was the golden era of explorations and records for the United States, chiefly because of the activities of the Army Air Service. To this must be added a very significant feature of U.S. air activity that was not present in Europe—the growing and healthy rivalry between the Army's flyers and the equally skillful Naval aviators who could now justifiably use landplanes because of aircraft carrier progress. By virtue of the stimulating activities and the limited but vital orders for advanced planes given to the industry by the Army and the Navy, America suddenly led in air progress.

By the end of 1923, of 42 air world records, no less than 34 had been established by the United States!

Here are some of them.

The top record that we succeeded in wresting from Europe was the speed record. This was done by the Army Air Service, at the National Air Meet held in 1922 at Selfridge Field, Detroit, winning the Pulitzer Race of 1922 from the Navy and several other entries, when Lt. Russell L. Maughan, flying a Curtiss biplane racer, established the record of 205.8 miles per hour around a 155-mile circuit. In this plane was introduced a signal and unique improvement in the radiator. The clumsy, speed-reducing radiator needed for its water-cooled, 450 h.p. D12 Curtiss 12-cylinder motor had been converted into the form of thin sleeves over the wing shape with no protuberance at all. This "skin radiator" had military vulnerability but as a design feature for higher speed it marked an advance for speed far outdistancing anything in Europe.

Mitchell had induced the Army to allocate enough money to permit the construction of several racing planes for this race meet. This was conspicuously accomplished. The new Curtiss racer was the outstanding contribution, but Mitchell, by his initiative at this time in giving a free hand to the industry,

Smithsonian's National Air and Space Museum

Alfred Verville and his pioneer monoplane (1922), forerunner of today's low-wing retractable-gear planes.

caused other designers to take distinct and stimulating steps. The Verville-Sperry monoplane, designed by the veteran Alfred Verville, showed the way for the coming decade. Mitchell had told him "design next year's plane now, and don't make it a damn bird cage with wires." This great engineer's concept marked the advent of a type of plane that was to come into almost universal use in following years—a low-wing cantilever monoplane with its landing gear retracting into its wing. Had the engine had the power of the Curtiss and wing radiators too, the Verville would have been faster by far. Thomas-Morse entered a metal-wing design of great originality. The Loening entry was a low-wing cantilever monoplane with a huge 600-horsepower Packard motor, with fixed landing gear—very simple in design, with excellent visibility for rounding pylons. But a new difficulty was disclosed in airplane construction for the first time on this plane: the dreaded wing flutter. The cantilever wings were not stiff enough to resist this heretofore unknown aileron-induced phenomenon. By use of hastily added bracing, this plane finished with a speed of 190 miles per hour, its fine Packard motor working perfectly, but to no avail.

Mitchell's comment to me was, "Don't be downhearted . . . you learned something, didn't you?" I certainly had, as had all of us.

Mitchell topped off his great boost for the American airplane industry by flying the Curtiss racer on the last day of this Selfridge Field meet at a world's record of 224 miles per hour. He flew with his usual flamboyant flair, making the Navy rivals very annoyed but even more ambitious. It became very evident at this meet that the Army-Navy rivalry for prestige, records and appropriations had become an opportunity for the air industry to seize and use to its advantage. This it did for years to come, without making it appear too obvious.

Other records piled up one after another in this period. The world's altitude record was raised to nearly 40,000 feet by the rival efforts of "Shorty" Schroeder and Lt. J. A. D. Macready, both from McCook Field, the Air Service Engineering Division. There, Sanford Moss of the General Electric Company had been encouraged to develop the Moss Supercharger, the invention that made these altitude records possible. The Supercharger could be used for the Liberty or any other motor. This new American device forced air volume into the engine at much higher pressure than the light air at high altitudes would provide, thus greatly increasing the power just when it was falling off.

As for endurance and distance records they fell to the U.S. also. The versatile Lieutenant Macready from the Engineering Division, together with Lt. Oakley Kelly, in a Fokker *T2* monoplane fitted out with a special Liberty motor and enormous fuel tanks, on October 6, 1922, at San Diego, California, established the endurance record for continuous flight of 35 hours and 18 minutes. In the same type of plane this team on May 3, 1923, arrived at San Diego. They had flown nonstop from New York in 26 hours and 50 minutes. Other records for load-carrying over various distances, altitudes attained with various types, seaplanes, landplanes, etc. continued to be made until, at the end of 1922, as already indicated, 34 out of

Smithsonian's National Air and Space Museum

The Army's transcontinental pioneer flight of the Fokker *T2*. Crossing the continent took five times longer than today.

U.S. Air Force

The 1923 Pulitzer race winner, Lt. Cyrus Bettis (217 m.p.h.) in Curtiss *RBC-1* Army racer; 500-horsepower D-12 engine.

42 world's records were held by U. S. Army, Navy, or civilian aviators.

This feverish activity, continuing through 1923, included the surprising St. Louis, Missouri, Air Pageant, held in the first week of October 1923. This was the great National Air Race event at which races were also to be run for the highest speed, the winner to get the prized Pulitzer Trophy (established by the owners of the *New York World* and the *St. Louis Post Dispatch*). But the eye-opener to the world was that in addition to about 170 service planes, an unlooked for total of over 100 civilian planes showed up. They were from the backlog of gypsies, barnstormers, private owners and new fixed-base flying operators that had, unannounced, been growing up in the vast rural areas of the country. This widespread development was little known to the Washington and service-oriented aviation people here or abroad. These were the unheralded pioneers that were in a few years to form the rich background for talent and enterprise in building the civilian aviation strength of the nation—the "good" gypsies or itinerant aviators and the amazingly many surviving "flexible base" operators who had weathered the hard times of the barnstorming era.

More records were established in 1923, which was to be the Navy's year. Just before the St. Louis meet, the Schneider Marine Flying Trophy race (named for the cup donated by the big French armament firm) had been staged at Cowes, England, on September 28. There Lt. David Rittenhouse, in a Curtiss twin-float seaplane with the D-12 Curtiss engine souped up to 465 horsepower, won against international competitors at the high speed of 177 miles per hour, a new seaplane record for the distance. Then came the Pulitzer race at St. Louis, where Navy Lt. Al Williams, famous as a stunt and test pilot, easily won the race at the speed of 247 miles an hour.

The world flight of the Army aviators was the next headliner for the Air Service. This was much ballyhooed because it was the first circuit of the globe. The actual story of this effort discloses a series of problems that beset the four planes that started out. They often had to go through the difficult operation of changing from wheel gear to pontoons and back again to adapt to the various terrains over which they had to fly. One plane was lost in Alaska and later another between the Orkney Islands and Iceland. So only two of the original four returned to finish at Seattle, 175 days after the start. The distance was 26,435 miles. Considering the unsuitable type they were for this venture, the Douglas cruisers (not being amphibious) did a fine job of overcoming their difficulties. Their Liberty motors

Douglas Company

The Douglas *World Cruiser*, in land condition. The same plane changed into twin-float seaplane for overwater flights.

came through with satisfactory reliability. Eric Nelson, engineer of the group, was the real hero in the way he managed to maintain the planes and overcome his construction and maintenance troubles.

The Army-Navy tug of war for records which was to mean so much for technical progress in the industry continued feverishly. The Navy, after winning from the Army at St. Louis in the Pulitzer race, was in the next year, 1924, to suffer a heartbreaking reversal. The annual Schneider Cup Seaplane race was held in Baltimore on the Chesapeake Bay. The two services were entered, with their Curtiss racers on floats, and the

U.S. Navy

Adm. William A. Moffett, creator of the big air Navy. He did much to counter Mitchell.

Navy felt sure of keeping its leadership. But Army Lt. Jimmy Doolittle, with his superior flying technique and skill, outflew everyone and won at a speed of 246 miles per hour. This was fast, indeed, for a seaplane, and of course established the world record for this class.

Other service efforts began to taper off somewhat as appropriations lessened. Mitchell had become so involved in his fight for a separate air service organization that he was growing into a common scold, rather than the inspiring and stimulating leader he had been for a good five years after the war. The industry, mindful of the fact that with the Army and Navy still separate, it had two customers and not wanting to lose either, steered a very neutral course—a sort of tightrope stunt of staying friends with and being sympathetic to both. Also, for the first time, Mitchell had met his equal in skill at propagandizing aeronautical prominence. This was the vigorous and effective Adm. William Moffett, Chief of the Navy Bureau of Aeronautics, ably seconded by Capt. John H. Towers. They knew their way around the halls of Congress as well as or better than Mitchell, and were not in the least interested in a separate Air Force (with the convincing Mitchell probably as its head).

Controversy boiled and slopped over into *Saturday Evening Post* articles, lectures, publicity handouts and criticisms in public by Mitchell, who had become too shrill and strident

U.S. Navy

The *Shenandoah* at its mooring mast (above) and at Caldwell, Ohio, after breaking up in a thunderstorm.

even for his friend General Patrick. In February 1925, after a great deal of soul searching on the part of the Army Staff and Secretary of War Weeks, the decision was made to reassign Mitchell for the good of the services. He reverted from his temporary rank of brigadier general to his permanent rank of colonel, and was ordered to a post at San Antonio, Texas.

As 1925 wore on the Navy did more spectacular flying than did the Army, and the most publicized activity centered on the trips and demonstrations of the Navy-built dirigible balloon of *Zeppelin* type, the *Shenandoah.* This giant, almost 700 feet long and with a capacity of over 2,000,000 cubic feet of gas, was the first *Zeppelin* type of craft to be filled with helium gas (not flammable, unlike hydrogen). The Navy and Admiral Moffett in particular were full of pride and enthusiasm for this lumbering behemoth that could cruise at only 50 or 60 miles an hour. She was sent all over the United States on various trips, tying up at special and expensive mooring masts scattered from California to Texas to Detroit, where Henry Ford had built a mast. Her home port was at Lakehurst, New Jersey. Commander Zachary Landsdowne was the skipper, and his every trip was widely featured in the press. On September 3, 1925, the *Shenandoah* was over Ohio where she got mixed up with a violent thunderstorm. The turbulent stresses were so great that the structure finally gave way and she broke in two, carrying Landsdowne and most of his crew to their doom.

Other activities of the Navy that worked out more creditably were the flight of the new Navy *PN7* flying boat, built at the Naval Aircraft Factory in Philadelphia, to Culebra, Panama, a 2,500-mile trip conducted with no mechanical difficulty at all. There was also the pioneer exploration of the Arctic by Adm. (then Lt. Cdr.) Richard Byrd in three Loening amphibian planes. A less successful effort was the abortive flight of Comdr. John Rodgers, who had to land his Navy flying boat in heavy seas in his attempt to fly from California to Hawaii. He had run out of fuel after covering 1,800 of the 2,100 miles, and "sailed" the remainder of the trip safely on the water.

In San Antonio, Texas, Mitchell picked on the *Shenandoah* and Rodgers failures to do what he had been itching to do for many months. He threw caution to the winds, knowing what he would be up against but hoping through a certain self-sacrifice to win some kind of progress toward the establishment of a separate Air Force. He called in newspaper reporters and issued his famous and oft-quoted statement, accusing his superiors of "incompetency, criminal negligence and almost treasonable administration of the national defense by the War and Navy departments." And more to the same effect. The frequently described court martial followed. Some of the industry leaders had to attend and testify, straining to the limit the efforts we all were making to keep out of this Government "family squable" and still remain friends with both of our customers. Mitchell lost and was found guilty of gross insubordination and improper conduct. He was sentenced to suspen-

Dwight W. Morrow, chairman of the Morrow Board, appointed by President Coolidge to draw up civil aviation legislation. Mr. Morrow became a Senator from New Jersey in 1930. Father of Mrs. Charles A. Lindbergh, Senator Morrow retained a strong interest in aviation.

sion from the Army with loss of pay for five years. The "stormy petrel," as Mitchell was so often called, resigned on January 27, 1926. He had decided to devote the rest of his activities to bringing his fight for a separate Air Force to public acceptance, in lectures, articles and books. He failed in this and died ten years later.

The aircraft industry went on with its growth after this sensational trial, Mitchell's voice having become less effective. But he bothered the industry by constantly criticizing American planes as "obsolete" or "inadequate" to a degree that almost ruined our hopes for enough prestige to build up the foreign market we badly needed. The large majority of world's records read fine in the press but failed to bring prosperity to the aircraft business. There still were valleys of depression and mountains of obstructions to cross.

Partly as a result of the Mitchell excitement, the Coolidge Administration decided to review aviation activities without delay and formulate policies that had been under consideration for over a year.

Presently we will hear how the Morrow Board was appointed, and how successful it was in reducing most of the chaos of the flying business. Its excellent policies and recommendations could well be marked as a lasting benefit of Mitchell's activities. Without his goading, the Morrow Board would probably not have been created that soon, if at all.

10 Private Flying: Ford, Guggenheim, Morrow

THE CONDITION of the aviation industry at this period of its growth was vague and uncertain with but one exception—nobody was making any real money. We have to go back to 1921 to get the picture of how important the 1924–26 period was to become.

Records enough had been made . . . but it must be repeated that this had brought in no significant home or export business. The service appropriations had decreased from $50,000,000 in 1921 to less than $29,000,000 in 1924. Of this amount, only about two or three million a year were used for hardware built by the aircraft and engine factories. Their total capacity had been whittled down, from the war potential of 25,000 planes a year to less than 1,200 planes a year five years later, and this quota was not filled. Total employment in the industry had reached a low of about 4,000 persons. In 1923, 587 new airplanes were delivered. By 1925 this was to increase insignificantly to only 780 units. The increase was connected to the gradual absorption of wartime surplus planes and their replacement by newcomers to the industry, whose advent was to prove so important in years to come.

Waco, Travelair (Beech), Laird, Cessna, and several other outfits, newly confident, rising stars of the future, were breaking in on the seventeen or more accepted Army and Navy contractors, including Wright Aeronautical, Curtiss, Douglas, Martin, Loening, and Vought. The newcomers had courage. They were actually building new planes for the despised barnstormers, Middle West farmers, and the surviving fixed-base operators. They made small but real profits, with very little acclaim. In fact, most aviation historians ignore them, failing to understand their importance. Forty years later, Cessna alone was to build 8,000 strictly commercial planes in a $140,000,000-a-year business employing 12,000 persons.

Recorded aviation history is also greatly lacking in giving an insight into the start during the 1920's of what was first called "private flying" by important owners and companies, and later designated "general aviation." The Curtiss promotion technique of selling new planes (not war surplus craft) to individuals started this trend. The few sales that were made went to sportsmen and flying aficionados, who purchased Curtiss *Seagull* flying boats and an occasional three-seat, land-type *Oriole*. Lack of landing fields caused this market to fade. Curtiss lost a lot of money at that time. Besides, those planes flew too slowly to be either sensational or useful. In fact, against a heavy head wind their high airspeed of 80 to 90 miles an hour soon became an overground speed of only 40 or 50 miles an hour. The fast-traveling air enthusiast would look down at the roads he was flying over, dismayed to see the despised, "out-of-date" automobile going right by him . . . very humiliating.

There had been an opportunity in early 1921 for a faster and more commodious private air vehicle. The Loening Aeronautical Engineering Corporation had proceeded timidly to move into the area. The Loening air yacht, a distinctive new type of monoplane pusher with a semi-enclosed 5-seat cabin and using a Ford Liberty motor (lent by the Army), was built with company funds. It tested out surprisingly well, showing a speed of over 135 miles an hour, 50 miles an hour faster than its early

The Loening air yacht at Palm Beach, 1922.

rivals. This so pleased David McCulloch (popular Navy air veteran of the *NC* transatlantic flights) that he became the sales agent of the Loening Company. While Dave's list of prospects read like a social register, his response to cynics was "Wake up . . . it's these people that have the real money to buy and the yachtlike instincts to maintain a ship properly." In its first altitude test this mono-seaplane made a four-passenger world's record of 20,000 feet. The demonstrating season started in the winter of 1921 in Palm Beach where Dave conducted many pleasant flights over Florida and to the Bahamas for leading millionaires. At the end of the next winter season, on April 17, 1922, the Loening air yacht achieved its most outstanding record. Piloted by Clifford Webster with Fred Golder as co-pilot, it flew from Palm Beach to New York, through storms, in nine hours—a record that was to stand for ten years. This was not all.

McCulloch's demonstrations continued over Long Island Sound during the summer into October 1922, when he won for this plane the Wright Efficiency Trophy of the Aero Club by making three round trips from Port Washington, New York

The first company-owned plane, the Wright Company's *Wilbur Wright.*

City, to New London, Connecticut (a 100-mile distance) and returning in one day, carrying 24 passengers—600 miles in 5 hours and 33 minutes' flying time.

These impressive performances resulted in purchase orders, first from Vincent Astor, who used Clifford Webster as his captain-copilot. Soon thereafter, Commodore Harold S. Vanderbilt also ordered a Loening air yacht, followed by Ross Judson of Detroit, Powell Crossley, and others.

The first strictly "company-owned" plane in America's air history was ordered by the Wright Aeronautical Corporation. Orville Wright flew in this Loening air yacht after it was christened the *Wilbur Wright* by Miss Katherine Wright. It was flown from the Hudson River to the October 1922 National Air Races in Michigan, where General Mitchell flew it. Much overwater operation was done in perfect form; the engine in this particular model was a 350-horsepower Wright Hispano, instead of the Liberty, and worked just as well. General Mitchell was thus convinced that this seaplane would have much value at Army fields near water, such as Langley Field, Virginia, and in Panama, Hawaii and the Philippines, and was helpful in having the Army order eight of these aircraft. To individuals the sales price was $19,500 each ($4.90

a pound). The Army contract, which included spares for the eight planes (with Liberty engines furnished by the Army) totaled $133,000, a fine bit of business for the small Loening Company.

Then, typical of the way the Army, spurred on by Mitchell at this time, helped the air industry, Lt. Victor Bertrandias and Lt. George McDonnell at Langley Field proceeded to establish more load-carrying seaplane world's records, 133 m.p.h. high speed and 1,000 kilometers nonstop in 6 hours.

As a result of this, the 1921 award of the Robert J. Collier Trophy, in recognition of the importance of this general aviation beginning, was given to the Loening Company.

Seeking markets other than the inconstant military one, Douglas and Fokker (now established as an American company) joined Curtiss, Loening and a few others in this high-priced private sales area. While they made successful prototypes with fine performances, the demand for planes of this class was not yet great enough for anyone to make a real profit. But such sales to American industrialists, millionaire sportsmen, and yachting figures gave an impetus to flying that had been noticeably lacking in Europe, where flying still retained its military flavor almost exclusively. We led the world by a large margin then and have continued to do so. This early start, regardless of wars, has grown constantly, until forty years later we attained a private or company-owned air fleet operating some 100,000 planes (more than all the rest of the world put together). But to achieve this we had to face some trying times and problems.

The account of what a mess aviation was in during the twenties is not complete without recognizing first the utter lack of insurability. Flying was classed as so great a risk that individuals had great difficulty being covered at all. Fire insurance was very expensive. Collision insurance was out of the question and liability coverage was set at prohibitive rates. This was understandable, because there was no national or state regulatory basis for the licensing or operation of aircraft. In July

1921 the Underwriters Laboratories and the National Board of Fire Underwriters stepped into this vacuum under the leadership of Reed Chambers, former World War I ace and insurance specialist. They established a Register of Aircraft Pilots and a list of commercial and private aircraft types. In its own words, the Underwriters Association "put aviation in the United States upon a definite footing . . . by requiring its members to register aircraft which they insured against fire, theft, collision and other risks," under quite rigid specifications. These were formulated from rules of construction, inspection, maintenance and operation that had been adopted internationally in the Versailles peace treaty (not signed by the United States) and from the Canadian air registration system. None of this was mandatory. But it was a signpost.

The need for national regulatory laws and some kind of industrial organization for the loosely growing and amateurish aircraft business became only too obvious. In 1921 two leaders in the air trade, Sam Bradley, manager of the Manufacturers Aircraft Association (the patent pool), and the great aviation editor Lester Gardner (with assistance from the National Advisory Committee for Aeronautics) promoted formation of the Aeronautical Chamber of Commerce. This was established in July 1921. The first president elected was myself, largely because, not being a member of the manufacturers' patent pool association, I was distinctly an independent. From its beginning this organization was to represent all branches of the industry. This it has continued to do through the ensuing forty-five years. Today's Aerospace Industries Association is the direct descendant of this original group. Its high standards and useful functions include the publication of authoritative "yearbooks." These are the main source of information, and gained prestige and influence in the business world. Historians would indeed be lost without these comprehensive summaries, tables, charts and analyses.

Shortly after Charles Lawrance had merged his engine company with Wright Aeronautical, and his nine-cylinder, air-cooled innovation began its growth into the famous Wright Whirlwind motor (Lindbergh's), he became president of the Chamber. Under his outstanding leadership, coupled with Lester Gardner's vigorous editorializing push, a significant step was taken in July 1924. They had invited the very influential Will Hays, former chairman of the Republican National Committee and former U.S. Postmaster General, to the University Club in New York to meet the leaders of the aircraft industry, there to discuss the serious situation existing. Will Hays agreed that if the industry would designate a small committee to work with him on the critical problems of the manufacturers and operators, he would arrange with President Calvin Coolidge to give them serious attention. The following were the members of this pioneering group: Charles L. Lawrance (chairman), Glenn L. Martin, Chance M. Vought, Frank Russell (president of M.A.A.), Albert P. Loening, and Carl Fritsche (Airships, Inc.). In due course a statement was formulated and presented to President Coolidge, who decided to meet with them after they had discussed the main points with Secretary of War Weeks and Secretary of the Navy Wilbur, Gen. Mason Patrick, Chief of the Air Service, and Adm. William Moffett, Chief of the Bureau of Aeronautics. Afterward the group went to the White House where the aircraft representatives were presented individually to the President. An amusing incident: Secretary Wilbur, who had gone along and tried to join in, was greeted promptly by a remark from the President that he had not been invited. He withdrew.

Coolidge, despite his reputation as a taciturn man, was actually very loquacious, and seemed to understand fully the needs, complaints and problems of the struggling airplane and engine enterprises in the United States. These can be summarized as follows.

The shocking list of fatalities exploited by the press were according to careful investigation due largely to pilot error in about 50 percent of the cases. The answer to this was the examination and licensing of pilots by the Federal Government.

Utterly carefree and without restriction, anyone could do any kind of flying he wanted, alone or with passengers. The planes could be falling apart, yet no person or law could condemn them. Engines might be failing from lack of routine maintenance. Navigation aids were unavailable. These failings were giving aviation such a bad reputation with the public and with business interests that progress was discouraging indeed for that part of aviation which was sound, not too dangerous, and very useful. Planes needed Federal inspection and licensing for safety. This would also permit more practical insurance rates and more favorable risks for banks to make loans on. We all knew that. But year after year, starting with the Wadsworth bill in 1921, this and other regulatory bills had been turned down repeatedly by an uninterested Congress.

The erratic way in which Army and Navy appropriations were doled out by Congress caused a "feast or famine" condition which wrecked the continuity of operation of airplane factories. Also, many Government contracts were being let in the old style low-price-bidding, competitive manner. A company either incompetent in figuring a profitable price or desperate for a contract even at a loss would ruin the proper price basis of the builders.

Gradually, from 1921 to 1926, the Navy had extended its own building of aeronautical items, planes, airships and flying boats, and their spare parts. This was now practiced to such an extent that when the great dirigible airship *Shenandoah* was built by the Naval Aircraft Factory, almost 90 percent of the Congressional appropriation for new aircraft never reached the air industry at all. The same was generally true of the Army, with its Air Service construction operations at McCook Field, Dayton.

Behind the scenes when President Coolidge first gave attention to these air industry conditions was a specially intelligent and sympathetic Secretary of Commerce, Herbert Hoover. Year after year Hoover had appealed for air commerce regulation, until in early 1925 he appointed a board of his own to probe into commercial aviation. In the foreword of his report he says, "It is evident that . . . aviation has been steadily approaching the point of self-supporting . . . commercial transportation. It is highly necessary that the government should provide certain services which are essential for its development . . . and there should be created without further delay a Bureau of Civil Aeronautics in the Department of Commerce through which the government shall make possible the development of commercial aviation by providing navigational aids and regulation."

Another problem that had bedeviled the sane progress of airplane evolution was the continuing accusations of scandal and inefficiency made by disgruntled "inventors" and publicity seekers, who clamored so much that Congressional hearings followed (over twenty in five years). None of these found any wrongdoings; all they accomplished was to muddy the waters. These repeated investigations catapulted the name of obscure Congressmen and cantankerous Senators into the limelight. Findings of the investigations were that the Manufacturers Aircraft Association was not a "pernicious trust" . . . there was no "favoritism" by the services in placing contracts . . . no "horrid blacklisting or discrimination" against unsuccessful inventors, and so on.

Moreover, in one company after another, glamorous newspaper column status was succeeded by the embarrassment of no money left in the bank and no bank sufficiently impressed with aviation's future to care much about it. The financial hazards of this weird air business caught Chance Vought, for example, in 1922. After a Navy order of ten *VE-7H* planes had been delivered and he was ready for some real production of a fine plane, the niggardly Congress cut appropriations and Vought was hung up with a starving factory. The Loening Company, in its then current profitable phase of air yacht work, came to its rival's rescue by lending Vought cash to meet his payroll: a not uncommon camaraderie among those of us who knew the quick emergencies we lived under. Could

Vought have made a commercial loan at a bank? Not a prayer. The loan was promptly paid back on Vought's next order.

The "down" side of the air yacht business caught the Loening Company two years later, when the market for that type froze up. The closing down of the promising New York-Newport airline venture because of an accident required a quick shift to some other type of plane to command a profitable future. No loans were needed, but only because the whole staff of the Loening plant agreed to work without pay for a few weeks. Thin ice was a widely used thoroughfare in those pioneer days! The shift was to the amphibian type of plane.

Looking back now, it seems not as courageous as it was mandatory for the stumbling aircraft trade to have gone to Washington and, contrary to all business precedent, actually petition the Federal Government to put it under restraints! The chronology of the year 1925 is indeed impressive, as so many events important for the future all happened at about this same time. First came the passage of the Kelly Bill in February, which started the transport of mail by private contractors and was soon to grow into passenger transportation and eventually that of cargo. The gigantic scale air transport was to reach was only two generations away.

In early June 1925 the public heard for the first time of a splendid private munificence in behalf of aeronautical development. It was announced that the Guggenheim School of Aeronautics was to be established at New York University, with an outright gift of $500,000. A half year later, Daniel Guggenheim, head of the family of copper millions, founded the Daniel Guggenheim Fund for the Promotion of Aeronautics, Incorporated, with a princely provision of $2,500,000 to be supplied as needed by the directors. Harry F. Guggenheim, his son, a Naval aviator in World War I, was named president of the Fund, with retired Adm. Hutchinson Cone as vice-president and executive officer. Two years later Cone was succeeded as vice-president by Adm. Emory S. Land. Among later directors were Senator Dwight Morrow, Orville Wright,

Trubee Davison, and also Charles A. Lindbergh. In his deed of gift, January 16, 1926, Daniel Guggenheim wrote Secretary of Commerce Hoover,

> So much remains to be done before civil aviation can realize the possibilities before it, that everyone must recognize that there intervenes a period of necessary study and experimentation.

Meanwhile, vital events that were to cast their influence on the air industry's actual progress (and which were not mixed up in the Washington bickering fed by Mitchell's continuing attacks on his superiors) occurred, impressively, one by one. The first advent of business confidence in the future of air transport came in May 1925. It was the announced organization of the National Air Transport, Incorporated, set up to carry mail and eventually passengers between large cities in America. Particularly heartening to the aircraft trade was the caliber of businessmen and financiers from New York, Chicago and other cities who were involved.

On June 1, 1925, another milestone was established when Henry Ford announced the start by the Ford Company of its own air express line between Dearborn and Cleveland—and between Dearborn and Chicago—using six of the new and highly promising Stout all-metal, Liberty-motored monoplanes. In addition, he stated his plan to have a Ford Reliability Tour to demonstrate air operations, starting later in September. Aircraft people all over the country were thrilled.

July 1 saw the official beginning of the nightly U.S. Air Mail service between New York and Chicago (which shortly would be taken over by a private company in accordance with the Kelly Bill).

September 3 was the tragic day of the *Shenandoah*'s wreck. On September 5 came Billy Mitchell's statement to the press in San Antonio, Texas, denouncing the administration of aviation in the War and Navy departments, which was to result in his court martial.

Then on September 12, President Coolidge, already primed by his earlier consideration of the needs of the aeronautical field and his 1924 conferences with Will Hays' committee, announced the appointment of the President's Aircraft Board, with his Dartmouth classmate, financier Dwight W. Morrow, as chairman. The other members of this board were Judge Arthur C. Denison, vice-chairman, Dr. Wm. F. Durand, secretary, Senator Hiram Bingham, Congressmen James Parker and Carl Vinson, Maj. Gen. James G. Harbord, Rear Adm. F. F. Fletcher, and Howard E. Coffin. This imposing group immediately received high praise from the press. Even Colonel Mitchell joined in, saying, "I am confident of its ability and integrity."

However, when Chance Vought and I saw the makeup of the board, we did not like the inclusion of our old friend Howard Coffin of the Aircraft Production Board of the late war. Were we to be caught in another bit of "automobile" trickery? Immediately we put our ears to the ground to find out what he would be up to. It did not take long to get a reading. The gossip was that he was holding conferences with C. M. Keys, president of the Curtiss Company. We knew what was troubling Keys. His big company, with vast empty floor space in the Buffalo plant, was suffering badly from the competition of Douglas, Martin, and particularly Vought and Loening. We had taken away more service contracts for new aircraft from his company than he felt proper. As he had told many air officers (who relayed it to us), he felt that Curtiss, by virtue of its large, empty plants, should get the bulk of the contracts as its right, not because Curtiss had better plane designs. Admittedly, at the moment it had not. But for the great Curtiss plant to have only 52 out of 400 new planes on order was not "good for the country."

This would be a threat to us, and Chance got busy. He arranged a special meeting of a few of us from Long Island and New York, to place the facts off the record, with Mr. Morrow on a Sunday morning at Mitchel Field (named after Mayor Mitchel of New York). Mr. Morrow, later to become

Senator and Ambassador, was utterly informal in a golfing sweater and very fatherly. He allayed our worries that the big fellows would take over the hearings, and he assured us that we all would have equal time. This is exactly what he did when we began testifying, carefully limiting each witness to the twenty minutes allowed. Keys had no time to expound his argument. We noticed that Coffin was annoyed, but we felt better as the hearing progressed. We heard Coffin ask Glenn Martin, "Is it not a fact, Mr. Martin, that it is a considerably more intricate an engineering and manufacturing proposition to produce a complete airplane than it is a motorcar?" Martin took a long, sarcastic look at him and answered, "I am positive it is." Had Coffin learned his lesson at last?

In the presentation of our industry group, we had divided among us the important points we wanted to make on behalf of advocating legislation beneficial to our future. It fell to me to present some vital statistics. From 1919 to 1924, inclusive, the services had spent a total of $473,000,000 on aeronautics. In this five-year period there was spent on design, development, and testing of new types for the Army and Navy a total of $3,700,000—less than 1 percent of the money Congress had appropriated!

"Where was the rest spent?" I was asked by Senator Bingham, to which I answered, "That is not our business; that is yours. The Government is our customer, and we can't discuss what you do." How I would like to have gone into the waste on dirigible airships; Government maintenance shops doing work the industry should have been assigned; the Army-Navy competition in building planes at their plants. I continued, "Mr. Lawrance has told you so rightly that the records of today are the performances of tomorrow. Well, America has held more world's records than the rest of the nations put together. But here we have Colonel Mitchell advertising us as 'engineers that know nothing' and that 'All our service planes are obsolete.' This just isn't true, and hurts us a lot. As for his remarks about Byrd's Arctic expedition with our planes, he can criticize all he wants, but only American aviators today have flown those

Smithsonian's National Air and Space Museum

A special favorite, used by Midwestern flying farmers on weekdays and for exhibition stunting or passenger carrying on weekends in the 1923–29 era, was the *Waco-Nine*, a small, handy three-seater with OX-5 engine.

Laird Company, Wichita

Pioneer Matty Laird seated in his Laird *Swallow*, a fine cross-country plane-trainer that was popular in the era when these well-built machines replaced the war surplus *Jennies*.

6,000 miles over the ice and surveyed 30,000 square miles of Greenland and Baffinland in terrible weather conditions."

The Morrow Board finished its excellent work on October 15, two weeks before Mitchell's trial began. The board's final report came out on December 2, in the midst of the sensational Mitchell proceedings. For a day or so, however, the Morrow report commanded more press notice than Mitchell, and rightly so. It was an intelligent and fair document, recommending much that we all felt the industry needed to get its start. Here are some of the recommendations, most of which were adopted by Congress in early 1926:

1. Secure the continuity of production by five-year plans and appropriations that would span a longer period than the "fits and starts" business we had been subjected to.
2. Stop direct competition from Government plants like the Naval Aircraft Factory in Philadelphia and McCook Field in Dayton.
3. Recognize and honor proprietary rights of design.
4. Limit competitive bidding so as to stop ruinous price cutting.
5. Establish an Aviation Bureau in the Department of Commerce to develop aids to navigation, as had been done in marine commerce, by lighting, airfields, mapping, radio aids, etc.
6. Require the licensing of airplane pilots and the certification of aircraft on a safe but reasonable basis.

Thus would the air industry and trade be put on an adequate basis in peacetime readily available for expansion in war.

There was a general sigh of relief in the industry. Aviation now had a brighter future. In the White House was a President who had seized the initiative on improving our enterprises by creating the outstanding Morrow Board; and in the Department of Commerce we had a great engineer in Herbert Hoover, whose understanding and vision of air transport can best be

Smithsonian's National Air and Space Museum

After he became President, Mr. Hoover invited this aviation group to the White House to discuss any pending problems. On the President's right is Charles L. Lawrance, and on his left is Clarence Young, chairman of the Civil Aeronautics Authority. Second from the left is the author.

illustrated by quoting from his testimony before the Morrow Board on September 23, 1925.

"Before we can expect to develop commercial aviation we must determine the air routes . . . develop a service for warnings of weather disturbance . . . prepare charts of these airways . . . secure the provision of landing fields and airports . . . provide for night movements by the lighting of our airways. We must develop a system of inspection of both planes and personnel, not only from the point of view of protecting human life but also of establishing confidence in aviation as a method of safe and reliable transport."

What was better still for us, this man was to become the next President.

Aviation stocks were a buy!

11 Came the "Whirlwind"

ALL THE BREAKS seemed to come at once in the ensuing two years. Following the Morrow Board's recommendations, Congress put through in record time three vitally important acts:

1. The Air Commerce Act of 1926, approved on May 20, 1926.
2. The Navy Five Year Aircraft Program, approved on June 24, 1926.
3. The Army Five Year Aircraft Program Act, approved July 2, 1926.

Senator Hiram Bingham (Conn.) assumed the leadership that pushed these bills to a final signing by a willing and pleased President Coolidge.

The National Advisory Committee, busy as it was with its useful and valid research in improving the technique of aircraft design—operating its fine wind tunnels, discovering new plane improvements, solving the "spinning" problem, devising the ring-cowl into the longer N.A.C.A. cowl for radial engines, and many other useful scientific research activities—also gave attention to Government legislation. Of the 1926 Air Commerce Act, it had this to say:

> This act provides the legislative cornerstone for the development of commercial aviation in America . . . on a sound basis. The Act asserts the doctrine of Federal Sovereignty in the air . . . to the exclusion of foreign nations . . . the right of the Federal Government to regulate interstate air commerce . . . the designating of airways . . . compels adherence to a single set of Federal flying rules on the part of all who use such airways . . . in air commerce . . . or private flying. It authorizes Federal lighting systems . . . maintenance of emergency landing fields . . . the transfer of postal airways to the jurisdiction of the Department of Commerce. It provides for the compulsory registration of aircraft engaged in interstate commerce . . . for the periodic examination and rating of airmen . . . and imposes upon the Secretary of Commerce the duty of fostering the development of air commerce in the United States.

On August 11, 1926, President Coolidge appointed William P. McCracken, Jr., a noted Washington aviation lawyer, as the first Assistant Secretary of Commerce for Aeronautics, a signal recognition of the status aviation had attained in the hierarchy of government. Promptly after this the initial U.S. appropriation for flying (other than war) was voted—$550,000 for aid to air navigation, administration, research and regulatory purposes of the act. It is remarkable that the licensing requirements for pilots and the specifications for "certification of airworthiness" for planes formulated at this early time have required very little change after forty years. A great tribute to McCracken and his aides, particularly the able Clarence Young, who shortly succeeded to the top post.

The Navy Five Year Act provided for the appointment of an Assistant Secretary of the Navy for Aeronautics, to which post the President named Edward P. Warner, a distinguished aviation scientist. It also provided for the procurement over a five-year period of more than 1,600 airplanes, at a rate of 200 to 300 a year, at a cost of about $17,000,000 a year. Production was planned in such a way that the Navy would have a force of 1,000 planes in service.

Added to the Navy Act was a provision authorizing the construction of two new rigid airships of 6,500,000-cubic-feet capacity at a total cost of $8,000,000. These were to be the *Akron* and its sister ship, the *Macon.* Like the *Shenandoah,* which had been a third their size, they were destined to end in stark tragedy, the worst of which was the death of a great Navy air leader, Rear Adm. William A. Moffett.

Right at this point we might pause to give attention to the effect on the future of the air industry's development the "rigid airship mania" had. It had almost none. The separation between heavier-than-air planes and lighter-than-air dirigibles was surprisingly sharp. The two fields went their separate ways with very little influence on each other. The techniques of their operations were different, the training of officers and crew entirely disparate. In the eyes of the airplane people, the airship boys were just wasting their time and money on slow "bubbles" that were such easy victims of weather and expensive beyond all common sense. To the Navy's dirigible enthusiasts (which regrettably included not only Admiral Moffett but many other victims) the impressive ships were the ideal long-range Naval scout that could roam over the seas at will. After more development they would hopefully become a kind of great merchant ship of the air, with enough room aboard to give passengers real comfort and luxury on a scale "that cramped little airplanes would never be able to equal." Time was to prove how wrong this was; and that to this day, the greatest comfort of all to an air passenger is the announcement that he has arrived! Slow aircraft just do not survive. Everyone did admit that the *Zeppelin* development had given to the plane makers a priceless material for light and strong construction—the alloy Duralumin—which in a few years was to be used universally for plane construction. To this extent the airplane industry was indebted to the airship industry. That's about as close together as they came, and explains why in this story of the airplane's growth to maturity so little reference need be made to balloons and their offspring. It is certain with our present technology that no balloons would ever attain speeds of 600 miles an hour, the very thing that was to give the airplane the right to thumb its nose at the weather. Nor conceivably would lighter-than-air craft go supersonic!

The Army Five Year Program provided, first of all, a change in organization, making the earlier "Army Air Service" into the "Army Air Corps." Its strength was increased to 1,650 officers and 15,000 enlisted men. The Army Aircraft Procurement program called for the maintenance of 1,600 serviceable planes with a replacement rate of about 400 planes a year, requiring an appropriation of 15 to 20 million dollars a year. Mindful of the importance and dignity now placed upon aviation by the Congress and by himself, President Coolidge appointed a prominent and highly regarded former war pilot and aviation leader, F. Trubee Davison, as the first Assistant Secretary of War for Air. Thus began the helpful career in Government air operations of the popular Trubee, whose intelligence and application was to lead to his becoming a general in World War II, and to worldwide recognition as one of America's most valuable "statesmen of the air."

The excitement incident to the start of various airlines was intense. The first three domestic operators opened for business within a few weeks of each other. The routes were designated C.A.M. for "contract air mail." Colonial Air Transport was C.A.M.-1 and started on June 18, 1926. Its primitive fleet boasted two single-engine Fokkers, and two tri-motor Fokkers, all with Wright Whirlwind air-cooled motors. In its first six months 60,000 miles were flown on the 192-mile route from Boston to New York with not a single forced landing due to engine failure (a tribute to Charles Lawrance's Whirlwind). There were 110 forced landings, however, the majority of which could be traced to the bad, foggy weather in this area and the lack of adequate lighting when operations began. The line carried 6,600 pounds of mail, but no passengers were carried until April 1927. Juan T. Trippe (soon to become the founder of Pan American Airways) was the first vice-president and manager.

C.A.M.-2 was the Robertson line from St. Louis to Chicago. Among the early pilots was a recent Army Air cadet graduate named Charles Lindbergh. Before the end of 1926, this line had flown 104,000 miles along a route of 278 miles. The planes first used were Liberty *DH-4's* of the type the Post Office had been using. Major William B. Robertson was the founder and president. A St. Louis group had joined him in furnishing $250,000 in cash on a $500,000 capitalization (much the same group that later advanced $15,000 to finance Lindbergh's ocean flight). Of 376 trips scheduled, only 25 were canceled or delayed—chiefly because of weather. This line and Colonial Air Transport were to be merged in 1931 with a then newly formed amalgamation—American Airlines.

C.A.M.-3's route was from Chicago to Dallas, pioneered by the National Air Transport, Inc. This company was the real leader, with $10,000,000 capital furnished by an impressive group of business tycoons from Chicago, New York, and other centers. Our old friend, Howard E. Coffin, was the first president, soon to be succeeded by Col. Paul Henderson after the latter had resigned as head of the Post Office Air Mail Division. This was before the "conflict of interest" prohibition was imposed so firmly on the industry. The presence of aircraft manufacturing officers on the board of a transport company was permitted, in fact welcomed. On the board of National Air Transport were Charles Lawrance, president of Wright Aeronautical, and C. M. Keys, president of Curtiss.

National Air Transport started out with fourteen planes including ten Curtiss *Carrier Pigeons,* with Liberty motors, supposed to carry 1,000 pounds of mail. Also used was an early three-engine Ford-Stout with Whirlwind engines, carrying 2,500 pounds. The Curtiss planes were soon to be replaced with new six-seat, cabin-type *Travelair* monoplanes with Whirlwinds. Some 500,000 miles of flying were covered in seven months of 1926, carrying 60,000 pounds of mail with 90 percent of the trips completed. Only one forced landing was serious, most of the others being due to weather. The following year, National Air Transport acquired from the Post Office the choice route from Chicago to New York.

Then Boeing came along in July of 1927 and won the bid on the big route from Chicago to San Francisco. To this route Boeing added by purchase and merger the extension from San Francisco to Seattle, which had been pioneered by Vern Gorst, originally as C.A.M.-8 under the name of Pacific Air Transport. Now all that was needed to have a complete transcontinental airline was to combine Boeing Air Transport with National Air Transport. The Boeing group did this in late 1928 by buying enough stock on the market to wrest National Air Transport away from the holding company that "owned" it, North American Aviation, dominated by C. M. Keys. With this done, the combination became the foundation of United Air Lines, the same line that is today one of our great East-West companies.

Several other companies were formed at this period, but by far the most notable and important for the future of the airline industry was Western Air Express. The first route of this conspicuously successful company was from Los Angeles to Salt Lake City. Its founder was Harris M. Hanshue, a tough business executive who was the first of these early pioneers to aim seriously at passenger carrying. He saw money in it and was so right! From the start of his operation, the line made a profit, unlike National Air Transport, which lost heavily until 1929 (when it finally turned in a profit of almost a million dollars). The reduction at that time of the airmail charge from ten to five cents had increased the poundage so much that all the lines began to make money. But none more so than the efficient Western Air Express. The 600-mile route from Los Angeles to Salt Lake City was opened April 17, 1926. At first this line used a specially designed new Douglas *M-2* mail plane, but very shortly changed over to the Fokker monoplane type. In its first seven months, Western Air flew 329,000 miles, carried 70,000

Western Air Express loads passengers on its Fokker F-10.

Underwood and Underwood, Inc.

Daniel Guggenheim, great philanthropist and contributor to aviation projects.

pounds of mail, and, significantly, 258 passengers. Two years later it was to carry 470,000 pounds of mail and express, flying 623,000 miles and carrying over 6,000 passengers. The mail pay was $3 a pound on the Salt Lake City run. But in 1927 Western had added to its operation a new and far more significant enterprise.

Aviation philanthropist Daniel Guggenheim had his own ideas about what would be good for airline development. Harry Guggenheim, his son, and others on the Aeronautics Promotion Fund's staff thought much of the risk and not too much of the advantages of passenger transportation. But Guggenheim Senior had noted that Western Air had completed its first year without an accident of any kind. Accordingly, on October 4, 1927, the Fund made an equipment trust loan (one of the

Smithsonian's National Air and Space Museum

Passenger transportation starts on the Fokker *F-10* with three air-cooled radial engines. Ten passengers were carried at a speed of 125 miles per hour.

earliest made) of $150,000 to Western Air to enable it to buy three Fokker *F-10* three-engine monoplanes with Wright Whirlwind engines. These planes were to be used solely on a model airline to carry passengers 365 miles between Los Angeles and San Francisco. The line was to be serviced with every safety precaution. The Bell Telephone laboratories installed a new radio system, which included many pioneer features. (For example, the shielding of spark plugs—to allow clear sending as well as receiving of messages—worked wonders). And ground stations established along the route and as far as 400 miles away were in constant weather and dispatching communication. Herbert Hoover, Jr., was in charge of radio engineering for the line. Voice transmission was also added. "Mr. Dan" was soon proved right as the passengers demanding tickets grew into the thousands, and the expected accidents did not materialize at all (that reliable Lawrance Whirlwind engine plus the radio). The loan was repaid within a year, and the growth of passenger carrying on Western and other lines rose from 18,679 people in 1927 to 385,000 in 1930, and to double that (almost 800,000) by 1935. Thirty years later, U.S. airlines were to carry over 100,000,000 passengers per year; more than one hundred times as many as in 1935.

Western Airlines finally merged with Transcontinental Air Transport in 1931 to form a now familiar airline, T.W.A. as "Transcontinental Western Air" became "Trans World Airlines" ten years later.

Another line established in 1926 that was to survive was Northwest Airways (now Northwest-Orient Airlines). Organized late in 1926, this line operated C.A.M.-9 from Chicago to St. Paul-Minneapolis, a route 377 miles long at its start. Stinson cabin planes were used with Wright Whirlwind engines, which were shortly to be replaced by Ford *Trimotor* monoplanes, also with Whirlwinds.

Transcontinental Air Transport (T.A.T.) was organized in 1928 by groups from both the Curtiss and the Wright Aeronautical companies. Lindbergh was to figure prominently in this line as its technical advisor. T.A.T. also had interested the Pennsylvania Railroad in becoming a partner with representation on the board. This was the beginning and the most prominent example of a combination of airlines and railroads designed to expedite the travel time of passengers and goods. It was done by making night runs on trains, which would then join up with planes for daylight cross-country runs, thus saving two days on the coast-to-coast trip. This sounded like a fine idea to some, including Lindbergh, and caused these companies to spend a lot of money quite futilely. The much touted "Lindbergh Air-Rail T.A.T. system" from New York to San Francisco took 48 hours. The first night of this trip had to be spent on a Pullman out of New York. Then the passenger would fly to Oklahoma, take a night train to New Mexico, and fly to California the next day. It was soon learned, as should have been foreseen, that passengers would much rather sit up at night and make the trip entirely by plane in about 26 hours. The air-rail scheme died a natural death in a few years, when the airways lighting was installed and when United Airlines, with some fine new Boeing 18-passenger transports, became capable of simple overnight trips to the Pacific Coast from Chicago.

The Ford activities, starting also in 1925-6, were extremely important. Ford's own private line between his factories had already been going in 1925, from Detroit to Chicago and to Cleveland. The Ford planes were the work of a great American pioneer, William B. Stout, who with George Prudden and

Thomas Towle in his group had made the first inroad building all-metal planes along the lines of the very successful German *Junkers.* The Stout group did a highly creditable job on the single Liberty engine monoplane, which developed progressively into the famous and long lasting Ford *Trimotor,* affectionately called the *Tin Goose* in later years. The first model *Trimotors* were equipped with Wright Whirlwind motors and carried 12 to 14 passengers. Later, as larger motors became available, the Ford carried 17 passengers, cruised at about 120 miles an hour, and landed easily in fields shorter than its rival, the three-engine Fokker, could manage. With its practical metal construction the Ford was much easier to maintain and weatherproof beyond our dreams of that day. Henry Ford sensed all this, organized for Stout a fine factory (now a museum) at Dearborn for the production of these favorite planes. All in all, Ford built about 185 of these sturdy planes and even today, some forty years later, there are about twenty Ford *Trimotors* still in use in various parts of North and Central America. Ford tried his hand at contract air mail lines. C.A.M.-6, between Detroit and Cleveland, was 91 miles, and C.A.M.-7, Detroit to Chicago, was 237 miles; these runs made connection with the transcontinental lines. After three years, however, Ford turned these over to other operators and concentrated on manufacturing. The Ford Reliability Tours, in which Henry Ford took such an interest, continued and were, indeed, a definite stimulus to general aviation.

While all these airlines were growing, a very important unit in the industry's factory inventory was developing in Hartford, Connecticut. In 1925 Fred Rentschler retired as chairman of Wright Aeronautical and joined George Mead, one of the leading Wright engineers, and several other expert engine men, to form the Pratt & Whitney Aircraft Company. Expert and talented they all were, and their company was a formidable addition to U.S. manufacturing resources. Aided chiefly by the Navy, Pratt & Whitney was to expand in the next forty years to become what it is today—the greatest en-

Aeronautical Chamber of Commerce

Ford's operation started with the single Liberty-motor Stout all-metal monoplane shown above.

Smithsonian's National Air and Space Museum

This Ford trimotor with Whirlwind engines was the prototype of the *Tin Goose,* which is still used in many areas of the world.

gine and propeller, jet turbine and rocket-producing unit in the industry. Many historians recite all kinds of scandals about extraordinary profits that were made by this great company. But the excellence of Pratt & Whitney (later United Aircraft) products through two generations is far more important than this kind of sniping. The first product, the 400-horsepower Wasp nine-cylinder, radial air-cooled engine was an instant success. The predominance of the Wright Whirlwind models, now named J4 and J5 and grown from 200 to 300 horsepower, was soon to be rivaled. (Charles L. Lawrance had received the 1927 Robert J. Collier Trophy for his fine pioneer Wright radial air-cooled engine, but his unique posi-

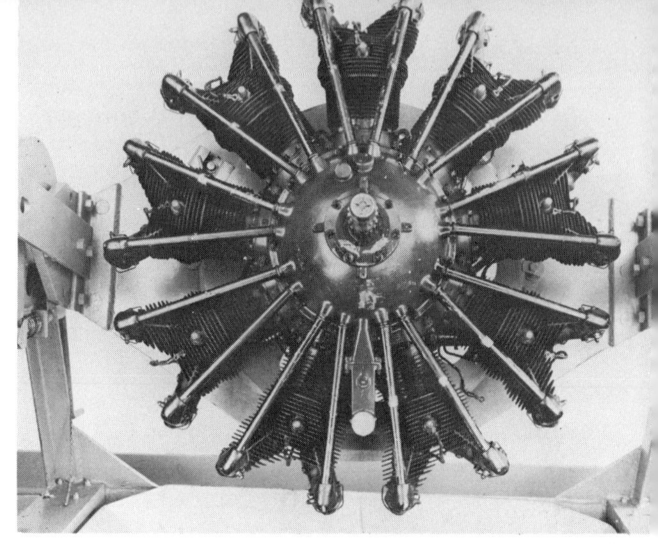

Smithsonian's National Air and Space Museum

The Wasp 400-horsepower engine which began the career of the United Aircraft Corporation of Hartford, Connecticut, in its Pratt & Whitney Division.

Smithsonian's National Air and Space Museum

The 9-cylinder Wasp grew in a few years to the 28-cylinder Wasp Major 4360, giving 3,600 horsepower. This marked the peak of piston-engine development before the advent of jet turbines.

tion was at an end. More power was needed.) The Wasp was very timely and went into widespread commercial and military use after a year of proving out by the services. On the larger airliners of 1929–31, the Wasp excelled in reliability, ease of maintenance and adaptability.

Then, in ensuing years, engines of increasingly great power were produced, such as the 500-horsepower Hornet.

By the time of World War II, when we had huge production schedules at the United Aircraft Company plants, the Pratt & Whitney radial engines had matured into twenty-eight-cylinder versions with horsepowers varying from the original Wasp of 400 horsepower to the Hornet and 18-cylinder R-2800 series, and finally to the air-cooled radial, the famous Wasp Major of

1944, which generated 3,500 horsepower from its 28-cylinders of four 7-cylinder banks. This descendant of the original Wasp marked the end of the radial air-cooled era. The jets were on their way!

The Wright Company, which in 1929 was to merge with Curtiss into the Curtiss-Wright Corporation (strange bedfellows, indeed, in the light of history) also continued through these formative years to evolve larger motors in the Cyclone series with multibanked cylinder configurations, with power equal to and sometimes larger than that of the Wasp family. But the Wright Whirlwind descendants never attained the excellence, reliability, and quantity-production-on-time of the Pratt & Whitney engines. By 1945, with the great World War II production included, Pratt & Whitney had delivered for military fighting, cargo-carrying, and commercial uses almost half a million air-cooled radial engines!

As for records and demonstrations of the airplane's capabilities, the world record marathon that had characterized the early twenties waned noticeably from 1926 on. These were not only dull record years but very poor ones for the United States. Our outstanding leadership had been lost to Europe, where a concerted effort to win the laurels from America had succeeded. The greatest nonstop distance was flown on October 29, 1926, when Lt. Dieudonné Costes, and Capt. Paul Rignot took off from Paris and landed at Djask, Iran, 3,313 miles away —only a few miles less than Lindbergh was to do seven months later. With new superchargers, French planes were making records approaching 40,000 feet in altitude. The Italian Macchi seaplanes were flying over 300 miles an hour, and a Farman plane in France had chalked up a duration of over 45 hours without landing. America was taking a different slant. At last it had realized that money and progress were made not by records but by the number of passengers carried and tons of cargo or mail lifted. Our more practical commercial instincts were waking up.

Important exploration flights were made at this time that

gave us plenty of prestige and worthwhile knowledge of air potential. In May 1926, America became the first nation to fly over the North Pole. Com. Richard Byrd continued the polar flying he had started in 1925 with Navy amphibians by organizing and successfully completing the Byrd-Bennett Arctic Expedition. On May 9, he and Floyd Bennett flew from Spitzbergen to the Pole and returned only 15 hours after departure. The plane used was a three-engine Fokker monoplane with Whirlwind engines, named the *Josephine Ford* after Edsel Ford's daughter. Other wealthy men financed the expedition, notably John D. Rockefeller, Jr., and Vincent Astor.

The first large-scale surveying expedition by the Navy started out from San Diego, California, on May 24, 1926, when three Loening amphibians under the command of Lt. Ben H. Wyatt took off to establish a base at Ketchikan, Alaska. The *National Geographic* magazine, in describing this operation, referred to it as "Conquering our Last Frontier." The breathtaking views of Alaskan mountains and glaciers disclosed many features. The planes spotted hidden lakes and passes that only air exploration would have shown and millions of acres of virgin timber. In his report Wyatt states, "Our work . . . was an acid test on the airplane itself and proved its ability to operate . . . under the most severe climatic conditions. After the completion of the work, the planes were flown back to San Diego and were ready to begin operations with the fleet the day of their arrival. . . . No forced landing from any cause whatsoever occurred." The reliable inverted Liberty was still doing its stuff. Two years later another Navy Alaska survey (this time the Loenings had Wasp engines) was conducted by Com. Arthur H. Radford (later Chief of the General Staff). Many other such flights were made by these amphibians because of their peculiar adaptability for such operations.

The most spectacular flight started in December 1926—the ambitious "Pan-American Good-Will Flight" by the U.S. Army Air Corps. This expedition, commanded by Maj. Herbert A. Dargue, included nine other officers, several later to become

U.S. Air Force

The Loening COA-1A amphibian biplane used on the Army's Good-Will Flight of 22,000 miles around all South America. Capt. Ira Eaker is at the bow and Lt. Muir Fairchild in the cockpit, in the harbor of Montevideo.

U.S. Navy

The Wasp-engined Loening *OL-8* survey and fleet plane used widely by the U.S. Navy from 1927 through 1935.

famous three and four-star generals, notably Capt. Ira C. Eaker, Lt. Muir S. Fairchild, and Lt. Ennis C. Whitehead. The planes were named after cities. For the first time, the route later to be exploited so widely by Pan American Airways, Panagra, and Braniff Airlines was opened by a squadron of Loening *COA-1* standard service, Liberty-engine amphibians (four in number with one in reserve). The officers did their own maintenance. Twenty-two thousand miles were flown on this arduous venture over much unknown territory where only the birds had looked down before. The object of this undertaking was to bring greetings and goodwill from the President and people of the United States to all the major South American nations. In all, the planes landed at one hundred different cities and towns, sometimes on their small and primitive airfields and often in their harbors or on adjacent beaches when no facilities were available.

An entirely unnecessary accident at Buenos Aires resulted in the collision of two planes of the squadron as they tried to avoid an Argentine plane flying through their formation. Capt. C. G. Woolsey and Lt. J. W. Benton were killed. The wrecked plane was replaced by a reserve plane later. The flight continued up the east coast, favorably received everywhere, particularly at Montevideo and Rio. After some long stretches of up to as much as 1,100 miles in a day, the planes reached the Caribbean, and on May 2, 1927, the Good-Will Flight landed at Bolling Field, Washington, D.C., to be greeted by President Coolidge, the Cabinet, and many diplomats. The officers received their well-merited Distinguished Flying Cross decorations.

Thousands of citizens a day file through the National Air Museum of the Smithsonian when on occasion the amphibian *San Francisco* is enshrined there, the very one that Gen. Ira Eaker and Gen. Muir Fairchild flew to Patagonia and back, exploring this new airway.

Early in 1927 the excitement about flying the Atlantic was consuming the attention of the aviation world. The tragic failure the year before of Captain René Fonck and his navigator, Lt. L. W. Curtin, did not deter others. It had been pretty well determined that Fonck's crackup when taking off in his three-motor Sikorsky biplane, overloaded as it was with fuel, had been due to a failure in the landing gear—a typical price of pioneering progress. The next on the list of aspirants for the ocean hop was none other than Comdr. Richard E. Byrd, whose polar-flight Fokker had been modified for longer range and named the *America.* His crew was to consist of Floyd Bennett and Lt. G. O. Noville as engineer. In a trial flight on April 1, 1927, carrying a full load and Anthony Fokker, the plane's builder, the plane made a very bad landing and was severely damaged. Six weeks later it was ready for a second try. Another mishap followed on April 26 when Lt. Comdr. Noel Davis and Lt. H. S. Wooster of the Navy wrecked their biplane, the *American Legion,* also in a test flight. Then the French aviators

Nungesser and Coli left Paris on May 6 to fly west across the ocean. They vanished and were never heard from. Other transatlantic attempts were to be made, all aimed at winning the tantalizing Orteig Prize of $25,000 for the first to span the route between New York and Paris.

Meanwhile, in late February 1927, a slim, blond, young airmail pilot arrived at the San Diego plant of the modest Ryan Airlines. This company had developed a further improvement on the strut-braced monoplane type that had been originated by the Loening Company in 1917 and had more or less lain dormant since. Ryan had found, as had Loening, that monoplanes were unpopular at that time with pilots, but he had gone ahead and built very efficient passenger-carrying planes of this type with Wright Whirlwind engines. These were so cheap to build and operate that Ryan established a small, flourishing airline between San Diego and Los Angeles. This operation also was proving the sound construction of the monoplane and the reliability of the engine.

So the young airmail pilot, Charles Augustus Lindbergh by name, using shrewd judgment, came to Ryan to have built the long-range, simple, efficient aircraft that he would need to span the Atlantic Ocean. What further clinched the proposition was that Ryan quoted a price of $10,000 for the plane, which was just within the amount of money the pilot could afford. He had raised $15,000 to cover the purchase of plane, fuel, traveling and living expenses, and many other items that would come up during the ensuing three months before his planned starting date. A small profit would be made by winning the $25,000; that could be divided among his backers.

Having had the opportunity in later months to discuss Lindbergh's whole plan with him, I feel quite certain that in his mind was no thought of failure, and he took every care to watch all expenses. I have seen a cost list of little items--stamps, telephone calls, sandwiches—as well as the bigger items, such as fuel, parts, clothing, etc. Determined he was to keep within the funds he had raised. Never was there any

Henry Miller

After his flights to Paris and to Mexico City, Lindbergh confers with the Secretaries for air, left to right: Edward Warner, Navy; William McCracken, Commerce; Trubee Davison, Army.

thought of personal glamour or prestige. Only one purpose—the attainment of a goal that would boost the drive for aviation: to have the public learn how wonderful it was! The rest of the *Spirit of St. Louis* story is too well known to review here: 3,500 or 3,600 miles (the exact distance traveled through the air was undeterminable, due to tail winds and course changes) flown in thirty-three and a half hours to an acclaim that has never yet been equaled.

The exaggeration of his glamour by the press and the public has been a difficult obstacle for Lindbergh to surmount in his fine efforts on behalf of aviation's sound growth. But forty years later we see how well he has maintained his dignity and conquered the battle against terrible odds to save his privacy. The oft-repeated verdict that it was this superbly managed flight that started the frenzied rise of aviation interest and speculation in the super-prosperity era of 1929 is mistaken. It had already been started by Herbert Hoover and President Coolidge and the 1926 Congress with their implementation of the Morrow Board's recommendations. The trend would surely not have stopped had Lindbergh not appeared, but what a spectacular and courageous performance the world would have been denied, had he not done so! His great contribution was to crystallize for all to see how successful aviation could be. To call him "Lucky Lindy" is wrong. Plucky he was; determined, dedicated, and confident.

12 Big Business Stumbles and Flops

THE EVENTFUL decade from 1926 to 1936 saw other beginnings that were to mean much to the future of the aircraft business. John Hambleton and his partner, Juan T. Trippe, both World War I Navy air cadets from Yale, had already broken into the passenger and mail business by establishing the New York to Boston operation of Colonial Airlines in 1926. They looked further afield later and saw the tremendous possibilities awaiting exploitation in flying south from Florida. So did several others, and a hectic race was on.

Two companies were already on the job. Florida Airways had been formed by Capt. Edward V. Rickenbacker and Maj. Reed Chambers. An airmail route, C.A.M.-10, was awarded to this Florida Airways company, whose operations from Miami to Jacksonville began in April 1926. After a few months an extension was granted to Atlanta. But this line did not flourish, and an extension to Havana was sought. Another rival for the route to Havana was a company called Pan-American Incorporated, founded by G. Grant Mason of Washington and Capt. J. K. Montgomery, former war pilot. They were fast workers, and before the others knew it they had won a one-way-only mail contract from the Cuban Government.

The third party seeking this Havana contract as a wedge to enter the South American market was a Wall Street holding company, The Aviation Corporation of the Americas. This outfit had money and plans but chiefly had Trippe, Hambleton and their associate, C. V. Whitney, as the principals. Among the early industry directors of this company were Sherman Fairchild and myself. Having sold out from Colonial Airways, this group started out after the foreign airmail contracts that the Post Office was getting ready to award. Trippe had his cap set for South America. He worked faster than his rivals, who were caught by surprise when they found that he and Hambleton had wangled the exclusive concession for landing rights in Cuba. The three rivals glared at each other, but not for long. Trippe's master hand at maneuvering and persuasion won out by his buying up the other two, not without certain instances of resentment.

Having disposed of competition, Trippe took the name Pan American Airways, which has been kept ever since, except for insertion of "World" to describe what Trippe intended and did accomplish in the following years when it became the first round-the-world airline. As an early director of Pan American Airways, I saw the manner in which Trippe was always two jumps ahead of his rivals, not only in political wire pulling but in his vision of the future and his demand for the development of bigger, faster, and more effective aircraft. Pan American was the first to use three-engine landplanes over water; first to use four-engine amphibians and *Clipper* flying boats; first to order commercial jet airliners; and today, the first to put money down on supersonic aircraft. Incidentally, this company was the first to arrange for passengers to be flown from a roof heliport in the city to outlying airports in helicopters.

Under the Foreign Air Mail Act of 1928, the Postmaster General was empowered to pay up to $2.00 a mile for the carriage of mail. Pan American's Key West to Havana contract, F.A.M.-4, came under the Act shortly after this Pan Am route

Smithsonian's National Air and Space Museum

At the start of the Miami-Havana service, Pan American used trimotor Fokker 12-passenger planes with Wasp engines. In a few years these were succeeded by flying boats until 1946, when land planes over oceans again took over.

was started in October 1927. From then on the system that had been worked out by Trippe proved very effective. Trippe, looking ahead, would get exclusive concessions from foreign governments long before the Post Office advertised for bidders. If they bid without the needed concessions, the Post Office could find only that the bids were unacceptable. The Postmaster General on occasion would encourage Trippe to buy out the ambitious competitor at a fair price. As the routes crept down from Havana to the southern continent's coast, others realized what a great market for air transport was up for grabs.

In 1929, Pan American ran into serious competition. Financed largely by James Rand of the powerful Remington Rand Company, a new line, the New York, Rio, and Buenos Aires Air Lines (NYRBA) started to carry passengers, at first with no mail contract. Their equipment, the efficient new Consolidated *Commodore* twin-Hornet-engine flying boats carrying 20 passengers, were first-class craft. The builder of these boats, Consolidated Aircraft Company, had as founder and president the famous Maj. Reuben Fleet, who had headed the Army's airmail service in 1918 and then became the contracting officer of the Air Service at McCook Field in the 1921-25 era. Fleet was a fighter and Pan American had no easy time in this battle. The manager of NYRBA was Capt. Ralph O'Neill, very competent and well regarded in South America. But the Post Office was adamant and would not give this line a contract. At first Postmaster General New under Coolidge and then his successor, Walter F. Brown under Hoover, stuck by their guns and found discretionary power under the airmail acts to stop this competition (undesirable for U.S. diplomacy) in foreign skies. Then the depression of the 1930's helped to weaken NYRBA. The solution was pressed by the Postmaster General, who insisted on the purchase of NYRBA by Pan American. This was accomplished and Trippe proceeded with his monopoly in South America. Miami soon became the base for Pan Am's operation.

In the years from 1926 to 1936 many other important advances were made. In June 1927, Lt. Lester J. Maitland and Lt. Albert F. Hegenberger flew from Oakland, California, to Honolulu, 2,407 miles in 25 hours, and 50 minutes in a three-engine Fokker. Admiral Byrd flew over the South Pole with Bernt Balchen on November 28, 1929. The longest endurance flight with refueling from the air was made by Maj. Carl Spaatz and Capt. Ira C. Eaker from January 1 to 7, 1929; the time, 151 hours, or 6¼ days, in the air, nonstop! Their plane was the Army Fokker trimotor, the *Question Mark*. On August 13, 1930, Capt. Frank Hawks startled our already record-surfeited world by flying nonstop from Los Angeles to New York in 12 hours and 25 minutes in his *Travelair* monoplane with Whirlwind motor. Then on September 1 to 2, 1930, the first nonstop transatlantic flight from east to west was made by the French aviators Capt. Dieudonné Costes and Maurice Bellonte. They flew in their Breguet biplane with Hispano engine from Paris to New York, 4,030 miles in 37½ hours.

The activities of the Guggenheim Fund continued to be beneficial. Aerodynamic wind-tunnel laboratories and technical aviation schools were established by endowments at California Institute of Technology, Massachusetts Institute of Technology, Georgia Institute of Technology, and New York University. The Safe Aircraft Competition took place during 1929. Its results were very disappointing. The Curtiss *Tanager* entry won the $100,000 prize, but as a contribution to safe flying or as an advance in aircraft design, it was never put into production or use. A far more important contribution of the Guggenheims after the Aeronautics Fund had been liquidated in 1931 occurred when, at the urging of Col. Lindbergh, Mr. Dan personally continued the financing (originally begun by the Smithsonian Institution) of the experiments of Professor Robert H. Goddard in chemical-fueled rocketry—pioneering work that began the American space age. The Fund, having done its work so admirably, had been used up. The philanthropical interest in advancing the air space age on the part of Mr. Daniel Guggenheim still remained.

The Collier Trophy for 1929 was awarded to the deserving National Advisory Committee for Aeronautics. The research done by N.A.C.A. scientists to reduce the head resistance and improve the cooling of the radial air-cooled engine was a valuable improvement for all types of aircraft, from small fighters to large passenger planes. It resulted in higher speeds, better fuel efficiency, control improvement, and cleaner looks. The N.A.C.A. Cowling, as it was called, was used from then on, both here and abroad. And much was done on wing improvement.

As for other details of airplane design, the principal trend of this decade was the final swing to the monoplane—in smaller sizes the strut-braced variety, and in larger sizes the cantilever internally braced wing. The retractable landing gear was just coming into vogue, and acceptable to opinionated airmen mostly because of the wider use of amphibian aircraft. This

Pan-American

The four-Hornet-engined Sikorsky *S-40*, the 38-passenger *Caribbean Clipper*, which took over Pan American's operation from Miami to Cuba and South America.

wider use was to last until the helicopter, with its ability to land anywhere, and the increasing number of land fields, made amphibians somewhat obsolete. The Loening plane had acquired many rivals before the decade ended. Sikorsky, in particular, developed a fine amphibian in single-motor size (the *S-38*) and in two motor-size (the widely used *S-39*). Sikorsky branched out into the huge *S-40*, which was to be used by Pan American so effectively on the Miami-Havana run. Other amphibians that achieved notable success were the Douglas *Dolphin* and the Fokker (by now named General Aircraft) twin-engine, cantilever monoplane.

The most important new features in design that came into prominence at this time were the metal-skin Duralumin structures, both on stressed-skin wings and on monocoque (skin covering carrying the stresses) metal bodies. Ford-Stout had led in this but was soon caught up with. When the Douglas *DC-3* arrived on the scene in 1933 to join the Boeing *247* airliner and the Martin *M-10* bomber, the airplane engineering fraternity knew they had arrived at the fundamentally correct airplane design. From then on, fabric-covered wings, steel-tube fuselages, and veneer-covered wings like Fokker's were gone for good.

It is surprising to find how long it took for many immensely practical airplane details, such as metal propellers and even brakes on wheels, to gain wide acceptance. The mere fact that pilots had become used to raising and lowering landing gears on amphibians led to the universal acceptance of this on landplanes years before it would otherwise have come. Usually there was a ten-year delay from proposal of a new idea to approval by fussy fliers; this delay throughout airplane history has always annoyed the engineers. The Loening amphibian was an instant success largely because the designer deliberately had moved away from the superior monoplane and had designed the wings in familiar *DH-4* biplane form merely to fool the pilots into quick acceptance. It worked . . . and through its ten-year life this plane was 10 miles per hour slower and 200 pounds heavier than the monoplane version would have been.

In this decade there also appeared many more twin and four-engine planes. They were heralded with much ballyhoo as a great step toward safety. Actually, safety with multiengine installation was not the fundamental reason why the engineers adopted this feature, although added safety had some merit. The real reason was that all indications on the economy of commercial plane operation showed clearly that larger aircraft meant more earnings, more customers, less maintenance per passenger mile, etc., a fundamental that exists even more pointedly today with the size of airliners growing to accommodate 500 passengers. The engines that were available at any period were limited in power. In the 1926–36 era, the Hornets and Cyclones had developed from 500 to 800 horsepower. In order

Boeing Company

Boeing *S-14 Atlantic Clipper* finally ceded to land planes.

to reach the size the operators wanted, the builders first made twin-motor, then four-motor types. If an engine on these multimotor planes failed, the pilot usually landed anyhow, although on some overwater flights the plane continued with the remaining power. In some planes, the Douglas *DC-3*, for example, the twin-motor installation was not a safety feature on takeoff. And multimotors did nothing at all for safety when the plane caught fire or ran into fog, or when the pilot had heart failure, or when the plane ran out of gas, or when instruments or radio failed. The safest way to attain safety to start with was to design a reliable motor and to install it with care. But when we had a good motor and needed to double the size of the plane, the solution was to double the number of motors. The practice holds to this day, as even individual jet engines are not powerful enough to satisfy the ravenous appetite of commercial requirements. So let us be clear on this point, where many historians are misinformed: a multimotor is not a *sine qua non* of safety. It is only the solution to economic size.

The hectic year of this decade was, of course, 1929. At its beginning, the wonderful era of selling aviation to an eager public was in full swing. Passengers were crowding the airlines way beyond the dreams of the most sanguine. More than that, businessmen and socialites of America had taken to the convenience of flying with many fewer compunctions than before. Important men and firms were purchasing expensive planes, in the $30,000 and even $100,000 bracket, in the free-spending "epoch that was to last forever." Expensive as well as inexpensive private flying took place in a golden glow of enthusiasm—the cost be damned. Millionaires Marshall Field, William K. Vanderbilt, Harold McCormick, Gar Wood, and aviator Charles Lindbergh were a few of the purchasers of Loening amphibian air yachts. Sikorsky, too, had a fine list of prominent owners, including Robert D. Huntington, Powell Crossley, Col. Edward Deeds (who carried his on his oceangoing yacht), and others. Before the bubble burst a dock, float, and station were established at the foot of Wall Street by Mayor Fiorello LaGuardia, and it was not unusual for as many as twenty or thirty privately owned planes to land in the East River every business morning to deliver their tycoons to the stock market that "would continue indefinitely to rise" enough to pay for all this luxury. Income was ignored. When money was needed, one "just sold a little off the top"; tax: 12½ percent.

The system for allowing the public to share in all this air prosperity was a relatively simple formula. Great, high-sounding holding companies were established with capitalizations of millions of shares that would combine into one package a group of well-known or about-to-prosper airplane, engine, and airline companies. There being no conflict of interest limitations on combining the interest and operations of manufacturers and the users of their products, the airlines would become sure customers for the factory if the factory's holding company controlled them. This was why Keys and Hoyt of Curtiss-Wright joined in on assembling a group of companies, consisting mainly of Curtiss for planes, Wright Aeronautical for engines (Whirlwind, Cyclone, etc.), Curtiss-Reed Propeller (metal), Keystone Aircraft (bombers), Travelair (Walter Beech), Moth Aircraft, with General Motors (Fokker), Transcontinental Air Transport, National Air Transport, Ford Instrument Company, Sperry Gyroscope Company, Eastern Air Transport (later Rickenbacker's Eastern Air Lines), and several smaller outfits. In the Keystone company was included the Loening Aeronautical Engineering Corporation, which had been sold to the bankers Hayden Stone and Company (Richard Hoyt) in 1928. This group of companies was presented to the investing public under the name of North American Aviation Company. Capitalized at $25,000,000, the stock could be bought at any broker's counter and had "diversification."

The big rival hook-up to North American was United Aircraft and Transport Corporation. This was the empire of William E. Boeing teamed up with Fred Rentschler (Pratt & Whitney), Hamilton Propeller, Chance Vought, Sikorsky Aircraft, and behind them the National City Bank (Deeds and Co.). The transport part was the Boeing Airline across the continent and the several additions that Boeing had acquired, including National Air Transport and combined into the United system, which was then our greatest airline.

The October 1929 crash affected the industry's investment picture in no uncertain manner; the downtrend on aviation securities continued well into 1932. Most of the stocks went down 50 percent, many of them 80 percent, and a few, like Curtiss-Wright, even more. This stock had been selling at over $30. It sank to $.75 a share. United Aircraft and Transport reached a high of $160 a share in May 1929. By 1932 it had sunk to $6. One of the other holding companies, Aviation Corporation of Delaware (not to be confused with The Aviation Corporation of the Americas), dropped from $20 a share to $1.40. So the bubble had burst.

What did all this do to the industry itself? Less than would be expected, because the bulk of the profitmaking business still lay in building planes for the military services. Appropriations were high and profits were higher than they had been at any time in the industry's history. The airlines were doing fairly well, too, with mail pay disguised so as not to look like a subsidy. Several highly profitable companies had not joined the Wall Street holding company mania. The Douglas Company,

Grumman

The G-21 Grumman amphibian *Goose* of 1936 with two Wasp, Jr. engines, a six-seater at first, has survived thirty years as a widely used utility aircraft.

which had "gone public" in 1928, the Consolidated Aircraft Company, and Glenn Martin stayed aloof from the big combinations. They were quietly earning from 12 percent to 30 percent on their government contracts. The big commercial orders still constituted less than half their business, and some of the most profitable manufacturers would not touch the airline field at all.

One of the new companies untouched by the 1929 panic was the Grumman Aircraft Engineering Corporation. LeRoy Grumman and Leon "Jake" Swirbul had been the managers of the Loening Company when it was merged with Hoyt's Keystone Aircraft, and thereby became a part of the Curtiss-Wright combine. In 1929 they decided to break away from this group and start their own company. Without assistance from any bankers, using only their private capital from a small group of friends, they established the very modest Grumman Aircraft Engineering Corporation in a garage building at Baldwin, Long Island. Grumman was the president with Swirbul as vice-president; other personnel included graduates of the old Loening Company: William T. Schwendler, engineer; and Julius Holpit, shop foreman; Albert Loening, as a director.

Grumman

The Grumman *Gulfstream,* with Rolls Royce Spey turbojet engine, continues a line of craft in the wide field of privately owned planes.

The original investment totaled about $50,000. In 1966, the stock market valued this company at $270,000,000. Profitable repair and wreck-rebuilding work done by this talented group resulted in a profit the first year. Then began its career as the prime builder of Navy planes and later, private luxury planes. The remarkable history of this company shows continuous dividends without missing a year from 1932 on, totaling some $100,000,000. The holder of original Grumman stock, therefore, would have had the value of his investment increased over seven thousand times. This growth was not forced in any way. It was completely free of any holding company or stock manipulation, never involved in the slightest scandal. Grumman's own personal skill and judgment in plane design and contract negotiation, combined with Swirbul's masterful handling of his work force (40,000 employees at one time), plus the fact that the owners of the business were in such large measure the ones who did the work, must be the explanation for this achievement. Grumman has never had a strike.

When the 1929 panic and the 1932 carryover panic had been digested, an important move was made for the industry's welfare. Urged, planned with great foresight, and put over with unerring ability was former magazine publisher Lester Gardner's organization of the Institute of the Aeronautical Sciences. This was a scientific society in which we all joined with enthusiasm, because it had long been needed. Jerome Hunsaker, Edward Warner, Charles Lawrance, Sherman Fairchild, were but a few of the aviation field's best protagonists who joined Gardner to give this an engineering background and
ences. This was a scientific society in which we all joined with
make it a scientific clearinghouse for our burgeoning industry and a firm and financially sound success. Now renamed the American Institute of Aeronautics and Astronautics, it has some 30,000 members. It has established the highest professional standards, awards prizes, trophies and honors, holds lectures and symposia, elects "fellows" as aviation's highest status symbol, and has raised aerospace technology to the top level of scientific eminence.

As we go on to see the air industry's rise to greatness and national vigor, we find that it did not attain mature stability until after it had gone through Franklin Roosevelt's silly, unwarranted and tragic 1934 airmail cancellations.

The scene at the foot of Wall Street, New York, in the early 1930's, when private owner-air commuters arrived for a business day.

Aerial Surveys, Inc.

Douglas Company

The growth of aircraft manufacturing is shown by that of Douglas. Bottom: the start at Santa Monica in 1925. Center: the next step to Santa Monica in 1935. By 1965 Douglas had several plants, the largest of which was at Long Beach.

13 Settling Into Maturity

IN 1935 the airplane building industry and the airlines using its products surmounted the last man-made obstacle to its growing up. Through the twenties a score of investigations had been held in halls of Congress. The last important (and quite nasty) one was staged by the Senate's Special Committee to Investigate Air Mail Contracts, headed by Senator Hugo L. Black of Alabama.

The Kelly Act of 1925 had been modified twice. First, up to 80 percent of mail income went to the airlines. Then, this being not enough, contracts were let at $3.00 a pound (Western Air Express) and $2.00 a mile with a 300-pound capacity for foreign mail (Pan American). Pressure to improve this situation caused the McNary-Watres Act of 1930 to be passed. It provided that the airlines would be paid on a space-available mileage basis. It mattered not whether the space was filled. Pay came in anyhow. This system, added to the fine profits growing out of the continuing Morrow-Board-inspired Five Year Programs of the Army and Navy, meant that despite the 1929 slump the actual earnings of the industry were at a high point, at least for the big companies. Postmaster General Walter F. Brown, the appointee of President Hoover, had deliberately followed a policy of soft-pedaling competitive bidding. He saw rightly how poorly many small outfits would do the job, compared to the excellent work of the few well-founded companies.

Franklin D. Roosevelt took office in 1933. He had planned to demolish completely any evidence of the success of the Hoover regime. But there remained one outstanding Hoover achievement—the way in which prosperity had surrounded the aviation field. Helped by complaints from disappointed bidders for mail contracts, his investigators got busy, with the help of Senator Black, and discovered that Brown in 1930 had held a somewhat secret meeting with the big airmail contractors to carve out a sensible group of routes that would strongly build up the industry (chiefly in the interest of national defense, to compete with Europe). This gave President Roosevelt a fine opportunity to imply that Hoover's regime may have been quite crooked. So the word got around about the infamous "Spoils Conference of 1930" and that the airmail contracts were illegal. Jim Farley was Roosevelt's Postmaster General.

The President acted. On February 9, 1934, the Post Office Department canceled all airmail contracts on domestic lines. Pan American was left alone on the excuse that it had not taken part in the "Spoils Conference."

Then Roosevelt made a very big mistake. He ordered the Army Air Corps to take over and carry the mail. They had no suitable planes. Worse than that, they had none of the important instruments, such as the Sperry "turn and bank indicator" that the industry had developed for thick-weather mail flying. Some 60 pilots were assigned to this operation. In two months 15 of them were killed. This was enough to convince the President of his error in judgment. A temporary airmail law was passed quickly by Congress to return the mail carrying to contractors, and the President appointed a Federal Aviation Commission to get him out of his quandry. Headed by Clark Howell, an Atlanta, Georgia, editor, and with Dr. J. C. Hunsaker, ex-Secretary Edward P. Warner and J. Carroll Cone among the members, it repeated the performance of the Morrow Board by the excellence of its recommendations.

Silently and subtly, less than a year later many of the same old veterans of the American air transport buildup were back in the business. The names of the companies had been changed slightly, and some of the closely coupled transport and manufacturing companies had been separated and split up. United Aircraft and Transport Corporation, for example, had been severed into United Aircraft Corporation of Hartford, Connecticut, and United Airlines Company of Chicago. Others suffered the same fate, but none disadvantageously. However, the Government had established a policy of not allowing "conflicting interests." If an individual was a director of an airline at the same time that he was a director of an airplane manufacturing company, he was presumed to be dishonest. This nonsensical restriction goes on to this day and serves as a monument to Roosevelt's lack of faith in business ethics.

It is noteworthy that from then on for decades, aviation seemed to have freed itself from the scandalmongering it had been subjected to for some twenty years. There were, to be sure, more investigations to come, but most of them were constructive, in the interest of national defense, or for extension of our constantly growing air operations, particularly in the commercial field, where for the next three decades we were to continue to lead the world.

A very important factor in the attainment of this leading position was furnished by our greatest aircraft builder, Donald Wills Douglas, Sr., when he gave flying men the endearing and enduring *DC-3,* affectionately called the *Gooney Bird.* First ordered by T.W.A. in 1935, it was a lifesaver for this line because of its much greater earning power. Unlike the three-engine Fokker *F10* and the Ford *Trimotor,* the *DC-3* had only two engines, and from the start it used the higher-powered Hornet and Cyclone engines (500 to 800 horsepower).

The *DC-3* has been the model for most airliners to this day—even those with new jet engines. Because of its comfort, reli-

Douglas Company

Donald Douglas, leading American aircraft manufacturer, now retired. He has left a heritage of air transport development.

ability, high speed (180 miles per hour), the smoothness of its two-engine mounting, its metal, low-cantilever-wing construction, the ease of landing-gear retraction, the positiveness of its controls, and above all the low maintenance cost, it swept the airline field. Almost every airline all over the world was soon on the *DC-3* list of customers. Then World War II began and the military version of this plane, designated the *C-47*, became the backbone in all theaters for air supply services, including the famous operation "over the hump" into China. There is not enough space to recite the endless achievements of this fabulous airplane. It adds up to this: over 10,000 of them were built, the largest production of a commercial airline plane in the world. Even in the near future this will be hard to beat. Of this number some 4,000 or 5,000 are still in use. There is no end to the usefulness of the *DC* series. For the *DC-2* Douglas had received the Collier Trophy in 1936. In the words of authors Carroll V. Glines and Wendell F. Mosely in their exciting book *The DC-3*, ". . . the only replacement for the DC-3 is another DC-3."

The hectic nature of aircraft development has now quieted down. For several years the design of transport aircraft passed through no violent changes until the advent of turbojet engines. Lockheed entered the transport field at first with the

Douglas Company

Three Douglas transport milestones. At the top the *DC-3* of 1936, the famous *Gooney Bird*. In the center the *DC-6* of 1948. Below, the *DC-8* of 1960, with four turbojet engines.

Smithsonian's National Air and Space Museum

The Lockheed *Electra XC-35,* first airplane with a pressurized cabin, received the 1937 Collier Trophy.

early piston *Electra,* a 12-passenger, low-wing, retractable-landing-gear monoplane of the type that had become prevalent. At first the *Electra* used two Wasp 400-horsepower motors, and like so many other similar planes, then grew to larger size and more power. The *Electra* supplemented rather than rivaled the *DC-3.* It was more of a short-haul plane. Lockheed also pioneered at this time the important pressurized cabin for high-altitude operation.

By 1940 the keen and sometimes cutthroat competition among Douglas, Lockheed and Boeing had calmed down. Boeing had progressed from its early (1932) leader, the low-wing, twin-engine *247-D* with partly retracting landing gear to new designs in 1933: much larger four-engine, low-wing transports, influenced by the great new bomber design which was to make such a hit with the Army, the famous four-engine *B-17 Flying Fortress,* later to become the backbone of our World War II bomber fleet.

In this pre-World War II period, Glenn Martin and Sikorsky were busy meeting the requirements of Pan American for transoceanic "clipper" flying boats to span the Pacific and the Atlantic. The increases in size that the airlines needed in order to make money soon caused all of the airliner designs to grow to be four-engined. Double banked, radial air-cooled engines themselves also became bigger and bigger as United Aircraft, (Pratt & Whitney) and Curtiss-Wright fought it out. Engines with 1,000 horsepower were soon being used, and with four of these (4,000 horsepower) the transports were soon grossing a total weight of almost 70,000 pounds.

Many records were made in these prewar years, too many to be described separately. Altitude had been raised to 47,000 feet and speed to 447 miles per hour. Several nonstop distance records of over 5,000 miles had been flown.

The most important new development just before we entered the war was the pioneer successful flight of Igor Sikorsky in his first *S-300* helicopter, made at Bridgeport, Connecticut, in 1940. His consistent series of helicopter designs from that date on has been one of the real contributions to flying progress, ranking in importance and influence with the early work of the Wrights and Curtiss.

Sikorsky made an equally important advance in the prewar decade with the design and construction of his epoch-making flying boats for Pan American Airways. This vital series of transports began with the four-engine *S-40* amphibian, carrying 40 passengers daily from Miami to Havana in the greatest luxury. Many features of this great plane were suggested or required by two technicians of Juan Trippe's magnificent operation—Col. Lindbergh, consultant, and Pan American's highly competent chief engineer, the late André Priester. While other airlines in this period were content to sit tight and work their fleet to the utmost when they had latched on to the type of plane that fulfilled their needs, this was not so with Trippe and his organization. Viewed in retrospect, the most telling impetus they gave to aircraft development was the way in which they would move right in on new engines, planes or operating accessories to make sure that no one got ahead of them. The practice has held to this day: Pan American was the first to jump the gun on the supersonic plane. They never miss . . . what's more important, they are usually right.

In 1937 Congress had passed a new law to advance and protect the sick and failing Merchant Marine. President Roosevelt took particular pride in pushing it. The organization established by this law was the Maritime Commission. It was charged with the duty of administering subsidies to help the shipping of the United States in its battles with the vicious rivalry of other nations who were undercutting our trade. To the post of the first chairman of the Maritime Commission, the President appointed the banker and business genius Joseph P. Kennedy (father of John F. Kennedy). The maritime law required also that the chairman report to the Congress his recommendations with regard to transoceanic aircraft and its relation to the Merchant Marine. To make the study and prepare this report, Kennedy appointed me to the post of Aircraft Advisor. With a staff headed by Robert Lees, we got to work. There was excited interest in this because there had been agitation on behalf of the Zeppelin and Goodyear airship companies to induce our government to subsidize a big, new dirigible balloon program. There had also been promotions of overseas airlines, particularly on the Atlantic, by steamship lines that felt this should be their province. At this time Pan American had already started service across the Pacific. The study was made and the report accepted. The result: no subsidies for the useless slow dirigibles . . . clear forecasting of the way airplanes would smother ship passenger competition . . . a slight delay in Trippe's plan to make Pan American a monopoly in the air . . . American Export steamship line denied a subsidy but encouraged to add aircraft to their fleet (which would have given the industry another customer for transoceanic flying boats).

1941—the war was upon us. So transport and private aviation ceased to figure in the steps the industry had to take. Expansion took place on a scale that was dictated right from the White House and was the order of the day. I was present there when the President met with an aircraft group he had summoned. Waving his finger and tossing his head in that characteristic way, he firmly ordered our future. "You will build 20,000 planes in 1942 and double that every year thereafter!" he proclaimed, and then went on to the effect that no excuses would be accepted and that all the money needed would be forthcoming. I could not help but recall that dim past year of 1917 and that futile scheming of the auto group. This time the air business had at once gone to the rightful workers. The record was a proud one: 22,000 planes were built in 1942, growing to 96,000 planes of all sizes in 1944, just as Roosevelt had ordered. He was the boss all right and we knew it. My own work was on the War Production Board, where I joined my old friend Ted Wright and my Dayton friend, Harold Talbott, Jr. (very much chastened by time and by then really an expert in matters aeronautical). Our job was to allocate materials for aircraft work and factories, see that the raw materials were available, and establish priorities to meet the service programs. We soon found that there was not enough of such raw materials as tungsten, columbium, and rock crystals to meet our requirements because quantities were being sunk in the South Atlantic. These rare items had to be flown over—that was the only solution. Hence, the War Production Board got into the cargo plane business. The first problem we confronted was that the Secretary of War had ordered stopped all production on the Douglas *DC-4* (the latest Douglas airliner before Pearl Harbor) and the Lockheed *Constellation* (big, new 70-passenger airliner), and had directed the W.P.B. not to allocate any more materials for their construction. This bright thought had originated from someone in General Arnold's Air Corps headquarters who obviously "knew" that cargo or passenger planes "had no value in war." Incredible but a fact. By the time we got through battling, we had constructed a wooden factory (steel was too scarce) at Park Ridge, Illinois (now O'Hare Field), to build Douglas *DC-4s*, then named the *C-54.* Other steps were taken to establish a flow of cargo by air from African collecting points to South America via Ascension Island in the southern Atlantic Ocean.

One of these projects was to commission Howard Hughes, in partnership with Henry Kaiser, to build a very simple flying boat on known conventional lines and of wood because Duralumin was so scarce. Also, the wood plane would be easier to rush to completion. It was to be an eight-engine plane the only purpose of which was to load up in Africa, fly across the ocean and back for the war duration, and then be scrapped. Everything was fine until Hughes began to show that he was a perfectionist. He wanted this great craft to be of the finest workmanship. We needed merely a flying cargo hold. Delays occurred, so many that finally aluminum had again become available. So we told Hughes he could get the aluminum and make this a fine boat. He stubbornly refused to change from the special wood tricks that he had devised. Then we decided to cancel the contract. The almost two years that had been lost then made the boat unnecessary. The Reconstruction Finance Corporation (R.F.C.) had been paying the bills. We learned later that after we had canceled the order, Hughes was still getting money from the R.F.C., whose head was Jesse Jones. Finally it was stopped. Hughes had made one short straight-away hop with the boat. The Senate held an investigation. After the first day the flying boat was lost in a maze of irrelevant charges about Hughes (T.W.A.) and Pan American controversies. We in the W.P.B. withdrew, didn't care anyhow. The war was over.

After 1946 the industry had to face the trying dismemberment of the giant war production setup that had done such a magnificent job. At one time over 2,000,000 people had been employed in the air and affiliated industries. The path back to normalcy was easier than we thought it would be. In the ensuing years the feeling of stability returned. Nobody got too

Smithsonian's National Air and Space Museum

The *XP-59*, America's first turbojet aircraft. It was built by Bell, and the engines were built by General Electric. The initial flying was done by Robert Stanley on October 1, 1942 at Muroc, California. This marked our entry into the jet age, where speeds rapidly exceeded 400 miles per hour.

excited about records. The airlines were getting back in the swing with ever more marvelous motors and instruments and navigation aids. The war surplus was not a problem, as it had been in World War I. Besides, the country was full of aviators who had been so well trained that the gypsy menace was nonexistent. The Federal Aviation Agency regulations attended to all of this. The final big change in this era had started in 1942 at Muroc, California, when Bob Stanley flew the Bell *XP*-59 *A* with the General Electric GE-1A engine. Here was the first U.S. jet. From then on the feverish race into the jet age pervaded the entire aircraft and airline industry. There had been a little hesitation on the grounds that although we could raise the speed record above 500 miles an hour, what good would it do, when just a bit further we would run into the "sound barrier"—that menacing wall where "air would break down and tear the plane to pieces?"

That wall was reached on October 14, 1947 when Capt. "Chuck" Yeager made the first flight through the sound barrier by flying faster than sound, more than 760 miles an hour at sea

Smithsonian's National Air and Space Museum

First to break the sound barrier was the *XF-1*, America's rocket-powered plane, built by Bell in cooperation with the Air Force and the NACA. In early tests, pilot "Chuck" Yeager flew this plane at more than 1,000 miles per hour at an altitude of more than 60,000 feet.

level. There was a slight control difficulty as the "solid" air that was supposed to fracture like broken glass was encountered. No such thing happened. The plane was not torn apart . . . nor will the thousands of others be noticeably affected that twenty years hence pass through this phase of flying as an everyday experience.

The well-staffed Government CAB bureaus of air safety (under various names as the years go by) have done a notably conscientious job of investigating aircraft accidents and analyzing their causes. This has also been done in Europe. The greatest example of this is the scientific excellence with which the British Government investigated the accidents to the early *Comet* jet airliners. This exhaustive research resulted in establishing the requirements for structural strength required by the pressure effect of changes in altitude. The U. S. safety investigations have resulted in continued improvement in aircraft safety so that risks in commercial aviation have been reduced year by year to a highly acceptable level. There are still risks in flying. Many are the dangers involved in any mechanical devices, but it is noticeable that in the aircraft industry, the insistence on safety both from the Government and the industry's bankers and stockholders has resulted in little, if any, tolerance for sloppy or dangerous workmanship.

The Flight Safety Foundation, under its creator and longtime director Jerome Lederer, has had much to do with the high standards that the industry is making a habit of. This private, nonprofit organization was started and is supported by private donations, the earliest, and a constant benefactor, being Laurance S. Rockefeller. The contributions of airlines, manufacturers, and other individuals have established this organization effectively during the last 20 years.

The combined efforts of the Flight Safety Foundation, the Government, and the Air Line Pilots Association, as well as other units in the industry, have resulted in a consistent reduction of the airline accident rate to the point now where a passenger travels in a medium where there is only one fatality for well over 200 million passenger miles of travel.

While statistics and methods of measuring comparable risks are very complex, the number of automobile fatalities is one passenger for every 40 million passenger miles. In the case of buses the rate is about the same. The low rate of fatalities measured in passenger miles for traveling in aircraft is frequently attacked as being a meaningless comparison on the grounds that it is *hours* of risk taken rather than *miles* that should be the criteria. This is a fallacy, because if it takes five hours to fly from New York to San Francisco, the same distance would require about five days in a car, and during those five days the passenger's exposure to risk is much greater than during the few hours in the aircraft.

Many are the safety features of flying still requiring further progress. Vigorous steps are being taken to reduce fire hazards in the air and on the ground in an accident. Jellied fuels that cannot be ignited so quickly are being developed. Much more effective exit doors and emergency evacuation procedures are being designed. Despite the enormous growth of passenger flying, the attention being given to safety is so paramount that the low-risk status now existing should be able to be maintained.

The progress in the late fifties and the early sixties can best be studied by looking at the growth and activities of several different aircraft companies that are widely known. The big wartime military contractors continued on Government orders, but expected these to taper off sooner or later. They turned most of their attention to the development and sales of large passenger airlines. Boeing, Douglas, Consolidated (Convair), and Lockheed soon got into vigorous competition in this field during the decades after World War II.

The most unexpected growth that emerged in this period was in "general aviation" . . . that all-embracing term meant to include private flying and business usage, farm application, charter, taxi work, etc. This kind of aviation activity grew quickly into a big industry of its own.

Much of its success should be attributed to the consistently practical production (at very low prices) of the simple, flat, double-opposed, four and six-cylinder air-cooled piston engines (gradually growing from 65 to 285 horsepower) that the Lycoming Company, Continental Motors and the Franklin Company had developed with such proven reliability and economy. Even in this advancing jet age, these prosaic little engines continue to furnish a sure background for safe flying for a very large proportion of travel through America's skies. Easy on maintenance . . . cheap in cost . . . and not objectionably noisy. Their main trouble is that they occasionally run out of gas!

An outstanding instance of growth, disclosing several angles of the industry's ripening, is that of Clyde Cessna, one of the original barnstorming fliers. By 1935 Cessna and his talented engineer Dwane Wallace had made their company into a full-fledged manufacturer, producing the famous Cessna *Airmaster*, a cantilever monoplane so fast and efficient that its leadership is still legendary. Their company grew suddenly into big pro-

Smithsonian's National Air and Space Museum
The Cessna *Airmaster* of 1928. A variety of engines was used.

Lycoming Company
The double opposed engines, such as this 6-cylinder Lycoming came also in 4-cylinder versions and have been widely used in the last two decades.

duction when war threats called for their training plane—a twin-motor, six-seat monoplane, the *T-50*. In 1941 a gross business of $13,600,000 resulted in a profit of $1,600,000. Then came the era of the Cessna strut-braced steel-spring landing gear monoplane, graceful, light and handy. Various types succeeded each other in a bewildering array into worldwide use. Impressively, by 1960, a gross of $103,000,000 earned a profit of $7,000,000, and by 1966 this profit was doubled on a total business of over $200,000,000. It is important to note that a significant corner was turned in 1960 because 75 percent of the sales were strictly commercial. The commanding need of Government business had faded. The Cessna commercial plane business is therefore one of the most surefooted in the world. In the last decade a steady profit of 5 to 7 percent has been earned in a highly competitive field (vs. Beech, Piper, Mooney, etc.).

In the words of Dwane Wallace, now chairman of the Cessna Company, "The real achievement in commercial air-

Cessna Company
The Cessna *Cardinal,* the forty-year-later version of the *Airmaster.*

craft growth has been our development of a worldwide distributor and dealer, sales and service organization. This probably has contributed to our growth more than any other single factor."

One hundred dollars invested in Cessna in 1937 would now be worth $12,000.

Walter Beech, Army flying instructor, and then a barnstormer, created the Travelair Company in the late twenties. After a few years he merged with the Curtiss-Wright group. In 1932 after the depression had taken its toll he and his wife, the brilliant Olive Ann Beech (who succeeded him as president in 1950 when he died), went to Wichita, Kansas, and with $25,000 capital established the Beech Aircraft Corporation. Their step by step advance is second only to that of Grumman. An investment of $100 in this company at its start would in 35 years have grown to over $400,000. This build-up was the result of an unusual sense of timing and design ability for a ready market. Their business increased tremendously during World War II, but because of the excellent performance of the Beech twin-motor *Model 18* both as a trainer for the military and as a private executive six to eight seater plane with 200 miles per hour speed, there was no serious letdown after the war. In fact since 1950, sales have increased tenfold. With 10,000 employees and over 2,300,000 square feet of floor space this company

Beech Company

The Beech *Bonanza* popular private plane with distinctive butterfly tail.

Piper Company

The famous original *Piper Cub* of the 1930's.

reached a fiscal 1966 gross business in commercial products and military-aerospace programs of $165,000,000 on which it made a net profit of about $9,000,000. One of the lessons that can be learned from this history is the importance of not varying models too much. Beech has been exceptional in marketing types like the *Twin 18* and the *Bonanza* for longer time than usual in the industry. They have done this by making appealing changes in details only so that the tooling and factory setup remained of value longer. Since its inception Beech has sold in 35 years more than 26,000 planes. Total sales volume has exceeded $2,000,000,000 during the last three decades.

Little was it thought in 1937 when the Piper Aircraft Corporation was formed that in thirty years this small, struggling concern could rightfully say, "More people have bought Pipers

Piper Company

The Piper *Cherokee* grown into the *Arrow* four-seater, cantilever low-wing retractable landing gear, 170 miles per hour speed with 180-horsepower, Lycoming 6-cylinder engine.

Fairchild Aircraft Company

The Fairchild *F-24,* four-seat private plane with inverted Fairchild Ranger 6-clyinder, 165-horsepower engine. This was a popular plane in the 1930's.

than any other plane." William T. Piper, its founder (active aviator at over eighty years of age), and his sons have built up this industrial unit in Lock Haven, Pennsylvania, with a branch in Vero Beach, Florida. Since its beginning this company has built 80,000 planes, a large number of which were the famous and loved *Piper Cub* on which so many young Americans learned the first rudiments of flying. Since then the *Cherokee,* a low-wing four-seater, is becoming almost as ubiquitous. During its early years the *Cub* sold for as low as $995.00. Now there are luxurious six-seat twin-engine Pipers that sell for over $100,000. It is notable that Piper continues to be unique; except for a relatively few liaison planes and trainers used in World War II and the Korean War by the Government, Piper has built up its business on general aviation exclusively. This light plane enterprise has grown into a $90,000,000 a year operation delivering almost 5,000 planes for a profit of $7,000,000. By 1970 this company expects to double or triple its business. With more than 20 percent of its sales going abroad, it can truly be said that its customers are the citizens of the world.

Many important highlights of the airplane industry's prob-

Fairchild Aircraft Company

The Fairchild C-*123* cargo plane, still a war favorite after twenty years.

lems are revealed by noting Sherman Fairchild's aircraft operations (distinct from his camera and electronic activities). In the early thirties Fairchild developed the *Model 24,* a fine sturdy four-seat strut-braced monoplane. Only about 100 a year were sold (one to me). Then in 1939 this company won an Air Corps training plane contract which grew large in World War II. This low wing monoplane, the *PT-19*, used the Fairchild Ranger engine (six-cylinder inverted air-cooled) which was developed independently in Fairchild's engine plant. Plane and engine together constituted a notable exception to the trend of airplane evolution which generally had decreed (unlike the auto business) that a combination of an airframe and an engine by the same manufacturer could never be a success. In the decade after 1948 Fairchild progressed to the *C-119* and *G-123* cargo planes. The latter plane has returned to wide usage after almost 20 years of active life as an outstanding load carrier. The Government contracts for these were modestly profitable. Fairchild has pointed out that military business is difficult because "in the defense business you must rely on weapons systems subject to extreme changes in the political climate, the world situation, and the evolution of military strategy." The present success and worldwide use of the Fairchild *F-27* transport plane and its developing models bear this out strikingly. In thirty years the Fairchild Company under various names has raised its gross from $800,000 to $216,000,000 and a loss in 1937 of $350,000 was turned into a profit of almost $7,000,000 in 1966.

During these recent decades the major aircraft builders have also had their ups and downs. Their development is more difficult to appraise in its influence on airplane evolution due to the complexity of mergers, diversifications into other fields and the advent of large space and missile contracts such as evident in the Martin, Convair, General Dynamics and Bell histories. This takes them out of the class of the individual virtuosos like Piper, Cessna, Grumman, and Beech. With the advent of the turbine-jet engine it was even more evident how they rivaled and pursued each other along the same lines. If Boeing came out with a 90-passenger plane, Douglas, Convair (General Dynamics) or Lockheed would be close behind with their versions using much the same engines.

Lockheed, General Dynamics, and Boeing all attained about the same rate of growth and affluence. In the last thirty years their book values have increased 70 to 80 times and their sales have been in the billions, often ten times greater than that of the small companies. These giant companies have become so involved in space, missile and other programs as to invalidate comparison. Douglas had bad years in 1959-60, and later in 1966. However in the ten years following 1956, Douglas delivered a gross business of $9,000,000,000 earning a net profit for the period of $23,000,000. Commenting on the commercial aircraft advances, Donald Douglas has said, "The commercial airlines sought to reduce their operating costs to a point where the airlift of passengers and freight would be a profitable venture. So, to the design requirements for speed and range were cranked in the economics of lowered operational costs. It was our experience that, even with the best of design effort, most improvement stemmed from evolution rather than revolution." How true this has been when we look back on the flowering of the *DC* series from the incomparable *DC-3* through sure steps to the *DC-4, DC-6, DC-7* and then the *DC-8* and 9. When the jet engines arrived on the scene these last two carried on their ancestor's excellence.

The McDonnell Company of St. Louis, Missouri, was

founded in 1939 by its still-active head, James S. McDonnell. It has been unique in that for two decades before 1967, over 90 percent of its business has been in Air Force, Navy and space contracts. Out of this little-mentioned factory poured professional military and space hardware that may not have made headlines but made a lot of money. Some 2,400 *Phantom F-4* fighters have outclassed American or European competitors, and many more are on order. Out of this McDonnell plant have also come the better known *Gemini* capsules of our space triumphs. In 1967, however, this company departed from its status as an exclusive Government contractor by merging with the Douglas Aircraft Company, whose business has been over 70 percent commercial. This giant combination will have a gross business of well over two billion dollars a year. And the products command what in earlier years would have been considered fantastic prices—$2,000,000 each for the little fighters and up to $10,000,000 each for the famed Douglas airliners.

Among other important companies in the fast-moving aircraft industry is the Bell Aerospace Corporation. Its helicopter contribution has been eminently useful both for the military and in commerce. Bell, too, has been increasingly prosperous, ranking second to Sikorsky in the helicopter part of the industry, with Vertol (now part of Boeing) and Kaman close behind.

The Martin company, now Martin-Marietta, has been through mergers and changes, making it less prominent now in strictly aircraft commerce activity.

The creation of another great pioneer, the late James H. (Dutch) Kindelberger, is North American Aviation Incorporated—classed as the largest warplane producer of the last two decades. Famous in World War II for the fabrication of training planes . . . the *B-25* Mitchell bomber (used in Doolittle's Tokyo raid) and the fast, long-range *Mustang P-51* fighter (still among the fastest race-winning propeller planes), North American had by the end of the war built 43,000 planes. This is the largest warplane production of any one aircraft unit in the

Boeing Company
The first giant passenger plane now building is the 500-passenger Boeing 747. Planes of this type should be on the airlines by 1972.

world. In the last two decades, North American has kept building thousands of *F-86 Sabre* jet and *F-100 Super Sabre* jet fighters. The small four to eight-seater *Saberliner* private executive jet transport is in production as are large contracts for space items, missiles, etc. Like so much of the industry, North American's profits have reached dizzy heights—$48,000,000 net earnings a year recently from the labors of 92,000 employees.

This, then, is what our rapidly expanding air industry looks like after almost sixty years since the first contract for a flying machine was completed and paid for. We have come a long way indeed. From the Wright *Model A* to the *DC-6's, DC-7's,* Boeing *377's* Lockheed *Constellations* and *Electras.* These were merely the prologue to the jets we use so much—those familiar *707*'s, *727*'s, and *DC-8*'s and *9*'s. Military developments continue ever faster, higher, and more sophisticated. Targets are hit more effectively and war supply loads and troops are carried in fantastic amounts.

All of these, however, are merely the curtain-raisers for incredible new supersonic marvels and giant "jumbo" planes that are straining to get off that confining drawing board.

There is no more striking indication of the distance we have traveled in airplane progress than to ponder over the fact that the Wrights' first plane could not only have been carried within the fuselage of the latest "giant" plane but could have completed its first flight within the length of its cavernous hold!

14 Only the Beginning Has Opened

CONTEMPLATING where this air road we have built is likely to lead us brings some startling thoughts. The age of the wheel and axle—the era of autos, railroads, trucks—may gradually be giving way to the age of wings—release from the ground barriers and their traffic snarls.

Our optimism must, however, be tempered by existing limitations, for as presently developed the air road is defeated by its own endless expanse—no road signs to guide the traveler, no fences to restrain him. The pilot airman is lost if he knows no radio mystique or is not proficient on instruments or electronic landing systems. Because of our lack of devices for preventing high-speed collision, he must be told by a control tower where to and when he is to move, whether he likes it or not. So until the present licensed professionalism inherent in existing safe air travel is simplified to include a more amateur realm, the persons allowed to operate planes will be limited by expertise and obedience to F.A.A. regulations. The plane is thus taken out of the class of ground vehicles, where the navigation is so facilitated by the marking of roads with signs, lines, road borders or tracks. As on the sea, increasing numbers of radio direction finders, omniranges and lights all help in the air, but the professional limitations are there, particularly in thick weather. Many are the predictions that air travel will never be free of them.

Maybe . . . but "never" is a very unwise word to use in this ever-expanding flying field—particularly when we picture how new techniques involving radio beams coupled with television, radar positioning indicators, underground circuits and new tricks with lasers may all feed into a screen in the cockpit to give the pilot his course, position and directions as casually read as if hung in the sky. The "Decca" system already does some of this.

Supersonic aircraft will approach and pass each other at the speed of a bullet. Only electronic instruments can see them. They also will direct them away from collision, automatically.

Because airplanes must keep up flying speed to stay up, the biggest obstacle of all to any great increase in the number of aircraft in the air is that there is not enough room! Airliners stacking up to await their turn on the runway at a big airport today use a minimum of 70 to 80 square miles of airspace each. This size of the holding pattern is necessary because the existing jet planes cannot be slowed down enough to use any less. Fortunately, there is hope on this. It is VTOL: Vertical Take-Off and Landing aircraft.

At present we are actually operating an incompletely controlled vehicle! That is, the airline pilot, suddenly seeing an obstacle, cannot at his own discretion slow down or stop in the air, turn around or back up. All other vehicles can do so, but not the airplane. The helicopter can of course stop in the air and back up under control. But the shaft-gear-driven helicopter of today is fundamentally too slow and complicated, and it costs much too much to operate. We are learning that the airplane may in the future be endowed with the vertical flying ability of the helicopter, without losing its speed and its acceptable economy of operation. The most promising field for aircraft ingenuity is in the devising of the fast airplane that will unfold its rotors or have other means for landing vertically.

U.S. Air Force

The original U.S. Army Sikorsky *R-4* type (1943), the first successful helicopter accepted by any government.

This is not much more complex than the retractable landing gear or swinging wing now in use, the weights of which can be enormously reduced when landing is done vertically by rotors.

What a change it would be to have this kind of a vehicle in all sizes for air travel. We would first of all be free of the airport—that crushing burden on communities, on federal and municipal grants, and on the taxes needed to support these 15,000-foot runway domains. With aircraft having the ability to stop and back up, the present holding-pattern traffic control would be relegated to the past. So would stacking up and waiting in line for takeoff. The VTOL airplane could land unhampered at its own dock, roof, or ticket-gate position next to a plane that had let down into a neighboring position only a few moments before. Wartime helicopter usage in Vietnam has taught us that apprehension about heavy blast effect from the downthrust generated by vertical-support air flow can be met by suitable fences, baffles, and ground-based crew protection.

Lockheed, Hughes, Sikorsky, Grumman, Bell, and Fairchild are but a few of the talented and imaginative aircraft builders, in addition to young inventors yet unheard from, who are working on solutions to the challenge of VTOL development. They are all hampered by lack of money. Government interest in VTOL involves nothing like the five billion dollars a year spent on space exploration. In comparison, a few paltry millions a year in a half-hearted manner is all that has been put

New York Airways

The tilt rotor VTOL pioneered by Bell and Hiller using the vertical position for direct lift; rotor-wing units swing 90 degrees to the horizontal for propeller thrust, giving wing support under high-speed conditions.

into this combining of the airplane and the helicopter into VTOL development.

Our vertical flying activity is having profound effect on military operations, as has been proved in the intense struggle in Southeast Asia. The helicopter operations, particularly the "air envelopments" that have been made more practicable, have already changed the aircraft mission's position in the Army's book. In essence the Army has become an air force. The overriding predominance of strategic bombardment appears to be on the wane; its destructive decisiveness, becoming less final every day, may never again be what it was in World War II. Low-level attacks against advancing or entrenched armies by fast aircraft, however, still have great effectiveness with ever more deadly weapon systems.

The aircraft industry must appraise these trends objectively and unemotionally. Immense production of bombers may be replaced in the aircraft industry by equally large production of vertical-flying armored tanks that will take an objective by envelopment instead of destroying it by bombs.

As for fighting planes, there still is and will always be the

Sikorsky News

The Sikorsky *Compound* 260 miles per hour VTOL developed from helicopter rotors already in use. Lift at cruising would be provided almost entirely by fixed wings.

Hughes Tool Company

The Hughes *Heliplane* is a tip-jet driven rotor with a fixed central delta-wing-shape lifting surface. A VTOL combination that also holds intriguing promise.

fundamental fact that "faster and higher" is the keynote to mastery of the air. And with this thought comes the interesting speculation of how far is "faster and higher" before we run into that pending international treaty prohibiting the use of space for military purposes. When *X-15* flew supersonic at 4,000 miles an hour at the dizzying altitude of 400,000 feet, this was just the beginning of what rocket motors would bring forth. To talk about no fighting allowed in space is idiotic—our fighters are already there!

Our progress to date on moon and space exploration has involved the emotional element of the competitive dither that Russia's *Sputnik* threw us into and its supposed influence on our international prestige. But setting aside the semi-panic of the "space race," we have gained several striking and useful advances. Electronic miniaturization, several steps of which have been proved in space navigation, plenty of valuable new techniques in many industries handling new materials—these are immense contributions; so, too, is the work on the extremely valuable "Comsat" communications satellites. America's future air industry may surely profit from space "spinoffs"; it has already done so.

Air commerce in the future holds many surprises, and many new noises! The advent of VTOL plane development will probably be universal. Fifty years from now we will look back with as much astonishment at the ridiculous airports we built as we do now at the elaborate, expensive and all but abandoned barge canals and interurban trolley systems.

Noise, however, raises its ugly head—doubly ugly because VTOL aircraft need power at its noisiest to take off and land. There is designing hope here. One of the most promising ways to reduce the initial cost of building and maintaining helicopters and their VTOL derivatives is to give up using shafts and gears that drive the blades around. In their place, the rotor can be spun by exhausting the turbine-engine jet force out of the tips of the rotor blades. While this at first wastes power, the "tip-jet" drive is entirely practical. Above all other factors, it greatly reduces the noise of the power drive. With the turbine engine itself enclosed in a soundproof structure, it is then possible to achieve an acceptable noise level for the neighbors to live with. Fortunately, this wasteful tip exhaust need be used only for those few moments of vertical rising or landing operations, when the rotor is needed for the vertical lift functions of the VTOL combination. When the forward speed in the helicopter mode has become high enough, the flow of driving gases at the rotor tips may be ducted out to a rear tailpipe just as in an ordinary jet airplane, at which time the craft, after a tricky transition, proceeds to fly on its wings in the airplane mode where it could even fly supersonic but in a more silent way.

The future will also bring the noise of supersonic "booms," a dangerous noise that will have to be designed out of the flying system unless the coming supersonic airplane, the SST, is to be restricted to flying over transoceanic or uninhabited areas of the world. Some new studies, modifying body shape to break up the single boom into several smaller ones, hold promise. But in the lexicon of aviation there is no word for "cannot do." Anyone who thinks that noise will hamper the fast flying economy and service obtained from traveling 1,800 miles an hour is not reading the signals right. One aspect of supersonic passenger flying, however, does give us concern. With the present swept-back wings, the force of turbulent gusts on the passengers' comfort at 600 miles per hour is acceptable enough. But when the plane travels three times as fast, the forces varying as the square of the speed will be nine times as great. Can the passenger take it, or will some kind of shock-absorbing on wings or seats be needed? Jet streams of high turbulence in clear air are prevalent too at the 70,000-foot altitude where the supersonic flying will take place. This also means that the wing and tail structures have to be braced for huge forces. The existing noise of airflow past the windows will be nine times greater in the coming SST. Too loud a roar?

A sidelight on the projected economy of flying to the Pacific Coast in an hour and a half or to Europe in less than three hours is this: the SST airline company need serve much fewer and less elaborate meals. In fact, there hardly will be time for coffee. Yet supersonic flying will be popular, just the same.

The constant rise in the volume of air travel will continue, as will its encouragement by the Government, because under war conditions the equipment of air commerce is so great an asset; and in peacetime air travel is a rich source of tax income. Although in 1967 we already had in our airline system some 2,000 airliners, the majority of which were jets, the growth

Boeing Company

Growth of the Boeing Transport

At the top is the Boeing *Stratocruiser,* the first luxurious postwar airliner of 1945. This two-deck, 80-passenger plane cruised at more than 360 miles per hour, but was outdistanced by the jets.

In the center is the standard Boeing 707, which is gradually increasing in size and now carries nearly 200 passengers.

Below is the Boeing *SST,* the supersonic 1,800-m.p.h. airplane now under construction. This plane with four giant General Electric 50,000-pound-thrust jet engines should be flying by 1975 or earlier. This will be the first transport plane with wings that sweep forward in flight for slow landing.

continues. At that time we carried about 100,000,000 passengers a year. The 15 to 20 percent growth each year which has been going on for several years means 200,000,000 passengers a year in this decade. As private and company flying increases, no doubt the rate of airline growth will taper off. Also, of course, a business recession would have its slowing effect. However, there is a more serious threat in the offing to air traffic. More thought is needed on the growing ease with which business can be legally accomplished by electronic gadgets. Documents 1,000 miles apart can be mutually signed by telautograph combined with closed-circuit television; even oaths can be taken before notaries. People can talk to each other in confidence over phones and via television, can read documents miles away, or can have them recorded. Colored samples of goods can be presented for sales. But what will this do to the airline business? Recent surveys show that 70 percent of airline customers are businessmen on their way to or from closing a deal. Visiting loved ones, to be sure, is not yet an electronic victim, and dancing or playing golf can't be done by wire. But before we accept the figures of how enormously air passenger traffic will grow, it would be well to give all possibilities much sobering thought.

Much the same lag in pushing development that has characterized VTOL acceptance also took place in air cargo evolvement. It is astounding to review how long it took the airplane industry and its customers to recognize and appreciate the rich future that awaited the use of aircraft to carry all manner of freight in all quarters of the globe. A few years after the first World War there was very significant activity in cargo operations in remote areas of South America highlighted by the activity of the German airline "Scadta" in Colombia and "TACA" in Central America. All were largely ignored and dismissed by our North American groups as well as those in Europe.

War plane development, the breaking of records, the air mail success, and possibilities of passenger flying, entranced everyone. The general conviction prevailed that airplanes lacked room enough in their slim bodies or sufficient capacities due to their weight limitations to make any serious dent either in earnings or tonnage to attract cargo carrying as a serious possibility.

Some of us in the air business did not share this view and in the early thirties many were the lectures and articles advocating cargoplane development that fell on deaf ears.

In May, 1940 as our involvement in World War II became evident, the New York Herald-Tribune held an "Air Transport Forum" at which I was invited to present a paper created an increased interest but with much adverse argument. However, over the country there was enough editorial comment to stimulate more realization of air cargo's possibilities.

Then after the war had unfolded its message—the manifold uses in moving military cargoes by aircraft in ever increasing tonnage—commercial interest grew rapidly and several strictly cargo types of planes appeared like the *Curtiss C-46* and the *Fairchild Boxcar C-119*. Passenger liners began to come out in freighter versions; and in 1947 some 22,000,000 ton-miles of miscellaneous express and cargo were carried by U.S. airline operators in addition to 64,000,000 ton-miles of air mail flown. By 1957 air cargo and mail reached over 400,000,000 ton-miles and in 1966 this had increased to over four billion ton-miles, ten times as much! The growth continues apace but with still a long way to go to cut seriously into the trillions of ton-miles moved by trucks and railroads.

Ever greater impetus will be given to this growth by the huge air freighters that are now under immediate development, the Lockheed C5-A military giant (the "Galaxy-1100", commercial version) and the equally large Boeing 747-F. The latter is the 400 seat passenger plane transformed into a cargo version.

Courtesy Mrs. Odgen Reid

In 1940 the great cartoonist "Ding" gave his impression of the coming air cargo age on the editorial page of the New York *Herald Tribune*.

Lockheed News Bureau

The Lockheed C5-A *Galaxy*—this giant 121-foot-long cargo plane carries more than 100 tons of payload. The 28-wheel landing gear folds into the body. Four 50,000-pound thrust engines give it a 600-m.p.h. speed.

The significance of their size is quite revealing. These planes carry up to 240,000 lbs. of cargo at 600 m.p.h. which means 72, 000 ton-miles an hour. The early C-119 of twenty years ago generated a mere 6,000 ton-miles an hour; so that in two short decades, the load capacity per plane has increased twelve fold. With these in the air inventory, air cargo will grow immensely.

Much improvement is being devised for the unloading of these cargo quantities more efficiently at airport terminals. But we will surely soon find the real bottleneck is the congestion when delivery is undertaken on the crowded airport to city approach roads. Here again VTOL offers a solution.

Lockheed News Bureau

From plane to truck to road delivery. Containers—the size of trailer truck loads—slide in and out of the capacious C5-A freighter through doors 19 feet wide and 13 feet high.

If freight planes can join with passenger planes in benefitting from such an advancement, the present concentrated all-in-one-terminal crowding would be solved by multi terminal distribution. Can we reach that happy state where everyone stops piling every landing operation onto that same 10,000 foot runway of a big airport?

Suggestions have been advocated that cargo terminals like private plane terminals be separate and distinct from airline passenger stations. Some advocate that the requirement of huge airfields be more reasonably waived for much smaller fields and city center docks or large roofs, by the development of STOL aircraft. This type unlike VTOL is really just a slow landing plane, that cannot hover or back up and once committed must proceed through its landing sequence. Its slow flying capability is derived from high lift wings, with slots and flaps and a fatal characteristic for city flying—a very light wing loading. This light loading makes STOL very sensitive to gusty air turbulence such as any windy city will have in abundance. Helicopters and likewise any rotor equipped VTOL aircraft are remarkably free of this limitation. STOL may be able to carry a slightly higher load but its weakness for overpowering turbulence and lack of hovering ability will certainly be found to reduce its present appeal as a means of landing aircraft in or very near city centers.

There is one more avenue to explore in seeking to bring modern aircraft and their precious loads more closely near the city centers that most of their operations are destined for. This is an old avenue now almost forgotten in the rush. What about water-based airplanes? The highly modern aero-engineer will look up with a sneer at any such ancient concept as the "seaplane". But if we stop looking at this type in terms of seakeeping ability at which its shortcomings were disastrous and instead merely consider its hull and water takeoff configuration as a different method of lifting into the air, we can envision quite different possibilities. To begin with we merely would need canals or free unobstructed water surfaces instead of concrete, for takeoff and landing. Many such are available (all year in the majority of active climates) and in many instances near or even adjacent to those very city centers that the concrete runways are being relentlessly pushed away from. Also there is often no property expense, no zoning troubles, less noise provocation. Too, we must not overlook that the land-type landing gear of a big transport is 10–15% of its structural weight, and a very expensive maintenance item. Since

Douglas Company

This STOL aircraft type now in production is the McDonnell Douglas *188*, derived from the French Breguet *941*. This photo shows flaps down, slots out, and engine power blowing on wings for added lift.

Federal Aviation Authority

This is a scene in New York at the 1966 STOL testing.

A 4,000,000-pound water-based freight plane carrying 1,000-ton load. (Study made several years ago.)

American Export-Isbrandsen Lines

Sikorsky *S-54* cargo helicopter demonstrating the loading of containers on a steamship.

the pressurized fuselage of a plane is now quite strong enough to take landing loads in smooth water with a stepped-bottom shape, almost this entire landing gear weight can be assigned to more load carrying. New materials make corrosion less serious. Also the old bother of propeller clearance from spray is gone with jet engines. This all bears a fresh look!

Too blind an acceptance of our wheeled and brake equipped landing gears stops us from contemplating that there will be other ways to takeoff and land. We come again to V T O L. The super modern plane of 1980 may well be envisioned by the engineers of that coming era on a quite different fundamental.

By then we may have understood that all the wheels and brakes, retracing mechanisms, flaps, slats, boundary layer controls, swinging wings, thrust reversers, etc. could all be thrown away in one package and replaced by a vertical flying system, of any of several types such as retractable rotors, direct lift jets, tilting propeller axis systems, etc. And probably at less weight and certainly at less cost. Would this then be the final airplane configuration, if such is possible in the dynamic aircraft design profession?

Will private flying—"general aviation"—with its approximately 100,000 planes keep on growing? In 1967 some 16,000 private planes were delivered from American factories—more than in all the rest of the world put together. But this is not much compared to 90,000,000 autos and 1,000,000 motorboats filling the highways and seaways. In twenty years, when the VTOL era is here in earnest, some 1,000,000 private planes will fill the air.

Costs of all this great progress have risen with relentless persistence. The empty airframe cost of $4 to $8 per pound fifty years ago has now risen to $30 or so per pound. Mechanics who started their air-age work with enthusiasm at $24 a week now look with jaundiced eyes at pay of $140 a week.

Government aviation organizations and activities for air commerce have risen to dizzying heights. Perhaps much too much so. Twenty years after World War II employed personnel in the Federal Aviation Agency, the Civil Aeronautics Board, and other agencies dealing with air regulations, licensing, accident investigation, route establishment, airways and airport developments, totaled over 43,000 persons, costing $708,000,000 a year. It is incredible to contemplate that all this was needed to regulate the use of 107,000 planes flown by some 500,000 licensed pilots.

As in previous air eras, the development of engines gives great impetus to changes in aircraft and their usages. Jet turbines succeeded piston engines in a sweep that is not over yet. What will succeed the jets? There are two development areas to be heard from in the not-too-distant future: nuclear power and rocket power. The use of nuclear fusion or fission engines has a wall to surmount that might prove too formidable. The requirements of shielding passengers and goods from the effects of radiation by necessarily heavy walls of lead or other insulating material is a crushing handicap for an airplane designer to overcome. As for rocket power, the fertile brain of man is already exploring this. As planes get faster, rocket power for "hypersonic flight" (6,000 miles an hour) becomes more feasible. The control of rocket power so that, once ignited, the explosion of the chemical can be controlled is another of the coming great inventions for flight.

The condition of the airplane industry (now grown into the aerospace industry) is healthy and well stabilized in the jet age, doing a gross business of $30,000,000,000 a year. The organization is huge and its greatness is still growing. It is significant that the volume of air-transport plane business and of the smaller private-plane business had by 1967 become about as large as military manufacturing. Of course the military has recently ordered large quantities of aircraft "off the shelf"—commercial developments requiring little change for a war theater. This is a turning point in the industry's history and a very favorable one.

The little struggling infant that first earned $30,000 for the Wrights in that Army contract of 1907 has expanded in sixty

New York Airways

A convincing augury. Helicopters can lift whole structures—even houses—and place them lightly and accurately on their foundations.

years to employ almost two million persons and to do a gross business a million times its original size.

There is no hesitation anymore. We have taken off into greatness. The "fields of air" have indeed opened.

The Author

GROVER LOENING was born on September 12, 1888, in Bremen, Germany, where his father was United States consul general. Shortly after receiving the first master's degree in aeronautics in America, from Columbia University, he became assistant to Orville Wright, progressing actively in the aviation industry for the ensuing half a century.

As the head of his own company during World War I and for many years after, Mr. Loening pioneered in the development of a variety of military, commercial, and private planes, including the famous Loening Amphibian. Serving as an aircraft adviser to the government on many occasions, the author has been a consultant to the Maritime Commission, the War Production Board (during World War II), and the National Advisory Committee for Aeronautics. Presidents Truman, Eisenhower, Kennedy, and Johnson all have appointed him to be one of only two civilian members of the Advisory Board of the National Air Museum. For his work in aviation, Mr. Loening has received many awards—among them the Collier Trophy, the Wright Memorial Trophy, the Air Force Medal, and the Guggenheim Medal.

The author is the father of three grown children and has eight grand-children. He makes his home in Key Biscayne, Florida.

Index

Figures in italics refer to pages on which illustrations occur.